AN ILLUSTRATED GUIDE TO
FOSSILS

AN
ILLUSTRATED
GUIDE
TO
FOSSILS

CHRIS PELLANT

DRAGON'S WORLD

Dragon's World Ltd
Limpsfield
Surrey RH8 ODY
Great Britain

This edition first published in The United States 1996
© Dragon's World 1995
© Text and photographs Chris Pellant 1995
© Illustrations Dragon's World 1995

Editor: Cathy Meeus
Designer: Megra Mitchell
Art Director: John Strange
Editorial Director: Pippa Rubinstein

**The catalogue record for this book is available from
the British Library**

ISBN 1 85028 248 X

Typeset by Dragon's World

Printed in Slovenia

CONTENTS

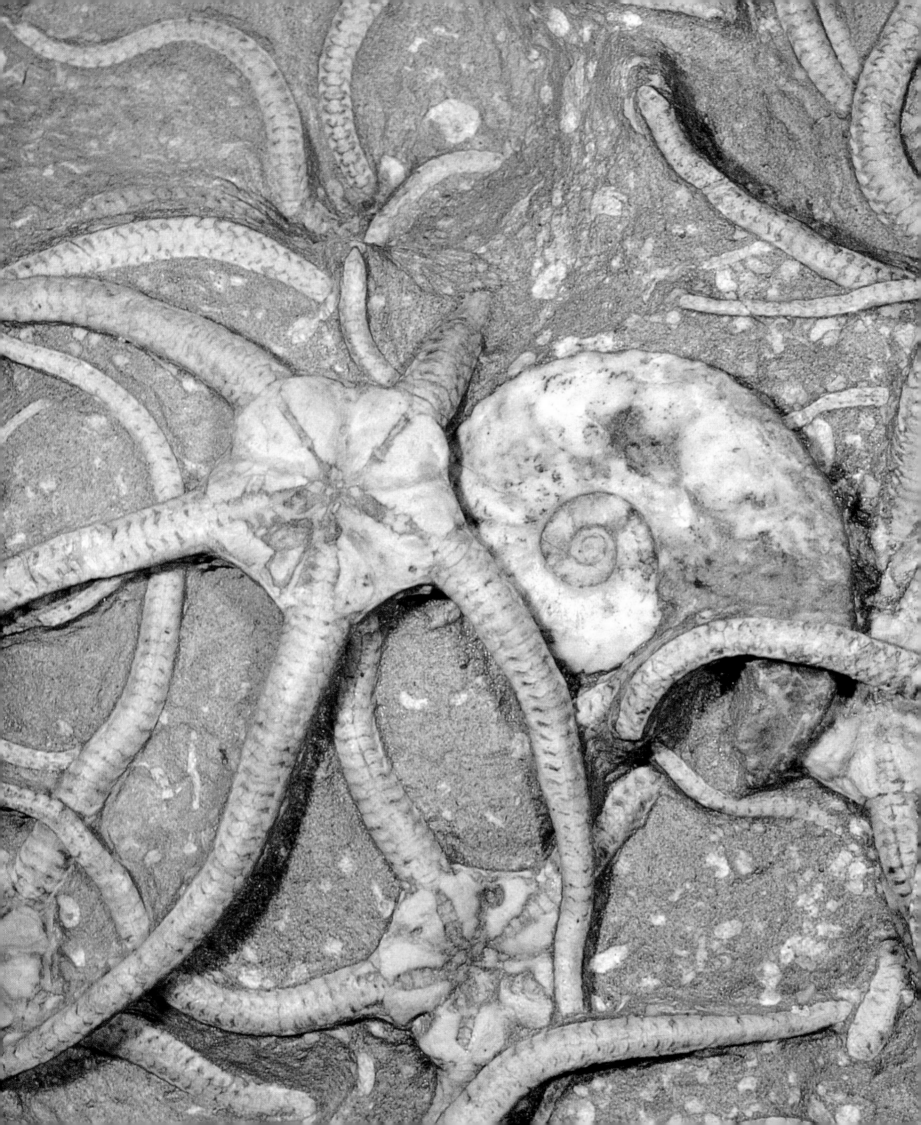

1 THE STUDY OF FOSSILS

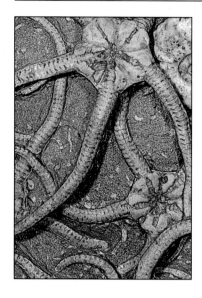

The word fossil means literally something that has been dug up, and can be defined as any evidence of past life. Fossils include such things as unaltered animal and plant remains, footprints, tracks, burrows, as well as shells, bones or tree trunks whose original material has been replaced by minerals. The science concerned with the study of fossils is known as palaeontology. Palaeontologists tend to exclude human remains and artefacts from their studies, since they are considered the province of the archaeologist. However, there is considerable overlap when dealing with the earliest hominid fossils.

Palaeontologists study organisms that are preserved in the rocks of the Earth's crust from a number of standpoints. They compare the remains of ancient creatures and plants with modern organisms in order to understand the structure of these extinct life forms and to develop insights into how they lived. Our knowledge of evolution is based on the fossil record of past life, and we see from this that evolution has not been a steady process but that the development of life on Earth has been punctuated by many sudden proliferations of various organisms and many mass extinctions.

The ecology of the past (palaeoecology) is also studied, and the interaction between the different groups of organisms that lived at the same period is interpreted. Fossils found in certain rock strata can tell us much about the conditions that prevailed when the rock was deposited. Many fossils are of great value in helping stratigraphers (geologists concerned with establishing the chronology of rock strata and past geological events) determine the correct sequence of rocks in a given area.

THE NATURAL HISTORY OF THE PAST

Fossils are biological material and as such constitute the natural history of past ages. The destruction of rare plants or animals provokes justifiable outrage, but when fossils are collected in great numbers and sold purely as objects of curiosity – a distressingly common occurrence – few complain. Even the unique Ediacaran fossils from the Pre-Cambrian era

in Australia have been plundered. Because the location of the specimens is often unrecorded, this thoughtless trade results in the loss of much valuable scientific evidence. There is no harm in serious amateurs collecting fossils; it is a rewarding and interesting study, but it is important to collect only in moderation. Consider photographing interesting finds, instead of actually collecting the specimens.

The identification of fossils may need expert help. Only a selection of the many fossils to be found are illustrated in this book, but it is hoped that you may be able to find a genus which fits your fossil or is very near to it. If you have trouble identifying a particular item, do not be afraid of showing it to the experts at your local museum or university. The most useful aid to identification is precise information on the location in which the specimen was found. Whenever I am presented with an unidentified fossil by a student or member of the public, my first question is invariably 'where did you find it?' There is always the chance of an amateur collector making an important find.

FOSSIL NAMES

Fossils, being biological remains, are named according to the rules of biological nomenclature established by the 18th-century Swedish naturalist Carolus Linnaeus. When he was compiling his catalogue of organisms, a major problem was that many creatures and plants, especially the more common

◁ **A mass of starfishes**
The fossilized remains of starfishes of the genus *Palaeocoma* have been preserved entangled with each other and with the shell of an ammonite.

ones, had different names in each language and no common scientific name. The system that he established, and which we still use today, employs standard Latin names.

Throughout this book the genus is given for each fossil, and in a few cases the name of the particular species. In the system laid down by Linnaeus, there are other, larger groupings such as phylum and kingdom.

AN EXAMPLE OF FOSSIL CLASSIFICATION

In this example, a common ammonite from the Jurassic period, *Dactylioceras commune*, is used to demonstrate the levels within the Linnaean system of classification.

The broadest category into which we can place this ammonite is the kingdom, in this example, Animalia (animals). The next category is that of phylum. *Dactylioceras* is in the phylum Mollusca, and is therefore a distant relative of clams, oysters and snails. Within this phylum, the ammonite is in the class known as Cephalopoda, indicating its similarity to squid, octopods and nautiloids. The next division is the order. *Dactylioceras* is in the order Ammonitida. After this comes the family, in this case, Eoderocerataceae, and then the genus, *Dactylioceras*. Identification to generic level is a good standard to achieve. The species name *commune* follows the generic name and correctly written both should be underlined or italicized.

△ **Unaltered shells**
In some cases, the original shell or bone of an organism is preserved unaltered. Here, the shells of several ammonites of the genus *Quenstedtoceras* are preserved in clay.

HOW FOSSILS ARE FORMED

The fossil record is a far from complete account of the organisms that have lived on Earth. Palaeontology is at times a frustrating science because of the gaps in the record. Sometimes it is possible only to guess at what a past ecosystem may have been like. Often in a particular stratum there is a good record of many different, highly advanced organisms, but we know that the environment represented by this rock must also have supported numerous other animals and plants of which no trace survives.

After death most organisms decompose or are fragmented, eaten, or otherwise destroyed and never become trapped by sediment in such a way as to form a fossil. Most sedimentary rocks form in the sea, and many fossils are found in these marine strata. This is largely because decomposition takes place less readily in the cold, low-oxygen conditions of the sea bed. The remains of plants and animals that lived on the land surface are more likely to have been destroyed by weathering and erosion, and while many sedimentary rocks formed on land, they tend to contain fewer fossils. Land animals have the best chance of being fossilized if buried in sands of river beds or the muddy sediments of lake beds.

The different processes that affect organisms after they die are highly complex, and fossilization takes place only in certain conditions. This is the reason why many

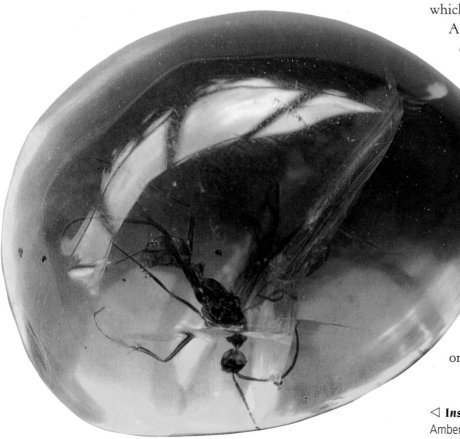

◁ **Insects in amber**
Amber is the fossilized resin from pine trees. Prehistoric insects, caught in the fragrant material as it oozed from the tree, are often preserved in amber.

organisms are not preserved. The study of what happens to an organism between its death and fossilization is called taphonomy. This encompasses the related processes of fossilization and diagenesis (changes in the rocks that surround the fossilized remains).

THE RIGHT CONDITIONS

For fossilization to occur a chemical balance has to be achieved between the organic material and the sediment in which it is buried. The conditions in the sediment are likely to be very different from those in which the creature lived. It assists the fossilization process if the organism has some hard parts, such

as a shell or tough stem, because these are more likely to survive until the remains have been buried in sediment. With luck, fossilization will occur after this burial.

The actual process of fossilization occurs as the original material of the organism is replaced by new minerals, and is therefore changed chemically. For example, a mollusc shell, such as that of a bivalve, gastropod or cephalopod, has a calcareous (lime-based) shell. The molecular chemical structure of the shell can be replaced molecule by molecule by another mineral, provided the size of the molecules taking over is much the same as that of the original material. In this way calcareous shells may change to pyrite (iron sulphide),

◁ **Preservation in quartz**
Replacement of the original organic material may occur if the remains of the organism are trapped in a sediment composed of minerals that are chemically more stable than the material of which the organism is made. This ammonite shell is preserved in quartz which has replaced the original aragonite shell. Small needle-like quartz crystals can be seen growing into the chambers.

◁ **Shell replacement by pyrite**
Pyrite commonly replaces shell material during fossilization. None of the original calcareous structure of this brachiopod remains.

△ **Mass fossilization**
Sometimes large numbers of creatures are preserved together. These fish were fossilized when the lake they inhabited dried up and their remains were subsequently covered with sediment.

hematite (iron oxide), or quartz (silicon dioxide). When this change occurs the original detail of the organism may be preserved without much distortion. This process of 'petrifaction' often occurs when fluids move through the strata containing the buried organism.

The shell, bone fragment or other organic material may also be removed in solution from the sediment. When this occurs, a small hollow, representing the space previously occupied by the organic material, is left in the sediment. This hollow may, especially if the sediment is fine-grained, retain details of the external markings of the shell. At a later time minerals or sediment may fill the cavity, producing a cast from the hollow, or mould.

The chemistry of living organisms is based on the element carbon, and very often all that is left of a creature or a plant is a fine carbon trace or outline. The other chemicals in their structure have been removed, leaving a carbon film fossil.

PERFECT PRESERVATION

In some cases, organisms retain their original form and structure after death. Insects are sometimes trapped in pine resin, which hardens to amber and entombs them in their original state. Mammals and insects may be caught in tar and peat. Without oxygen to promote the bacterial activity that leads to decomposition, their bodies survive intact. There are also examples of mammoths preserved, frozen in permafrost.

◁ **Shells in limestone**
This is part of a fossilized shell bank. Numerous elongated gastropod shells, as well as smaller bivalves, can be seen embedded in limestone.

▷ **Three-dimensional preservation**
Hollow spaces left when the soft body of the organism has decayed – for example, within shells – may fill with sediment and may thus be preserved in three dimensions. This infilling may prevent the structure from being crushed. In some cases, the mould records details of the inner surface of the shell. Here, a large number of *Protocardia*, a bivalve mollusc, have been infilled with fine-grained sandstone. Erosion has then cut through the rock to reveal the shells as thin, pale, heart-shaped cross-sections.

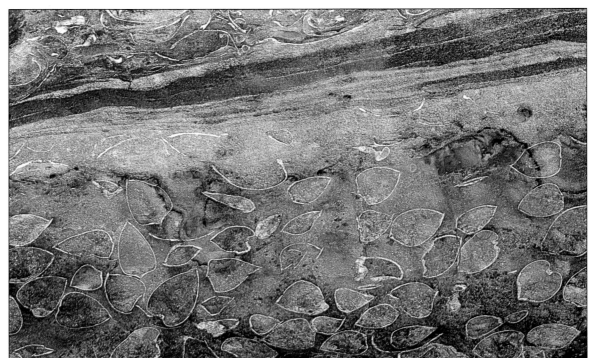

Organisms with hard structures stand the best chance of becoming fossilized. However, there are many cases of the preservation of delicate soft-bodied plants and creatures. This occurs only in rather unusual circumstances. One of the best known cases of this kind is that of the Burgess Shale of British Columbia, where during Lower Palaeozoic times, numerous soft-bodied organisms were swept down an undersea cliff by avalanches of fine mud, and were preserved in great detail (see page 83). The fine Jurassic limestones found in Germany at Solnhofen contain fossilized jellyfish, worms, insects, and the famous impressions of feathers belonging to the bird *Archaeopteryx*. These unusual limestone formations and their special fossil deposits are discussed more fully in the box on page 94.

◁ *Coral in hematite*
This is a highly magnified view of a fossil coral that has been replaced by hematite (iron oxide). The thin lines, now made of iron ore, are the septa of the coral, and were originally made of calcite.

▽ *Carbonization*
Often all that remains of leaves and other plant tissue is the carbon contained in the original chemical structure. Here, delicate plant fossils are preserved in layers of fine-grained shale.

THE ROCKS IN WHICH FOSSILS OCCUR

△ **Grand Canyon**
The horizontal strata in the steep sides of the gorge of the Colorado River are weathered and eroded to produce sediment, which the river carries away to be deposited as new rock layers.

There are three main groups of rock: igneous rocks, mainly formed by the solidification of lava or magma, metamorphic rocks, which are formed by heat or pressure (or both forces together) altering pre-formed rocks, and sedimentary rocks. Sedimentary rocks form on the Earth's surface and are therefore those that contain fossils. They are distinguished from igneous and metamorphic rocks by their stratification or bedding. This structure represents the original layers in which the sediment was deposited. Some slightly metamorphosed rocks, such as slate, have a structure called cleavage, where layers of rock have become aligned under pressure. This cleavage may look rather like bedding. Volcanic dust and ash, strictly the product of igneous activity, can be deposited in layers and may contain fossils.

TYPES OF SEDIMENTARY ROCK

Sedimentary rocks can be divided into three categories according to the method of formation and the materials of which they are made. Fossils have been found in all three types. Detrital, or fragmentary, sediments are made of sand, mud, pebbles and other grains that have worn off previously formed rocks of any type, as a result of the forces of weathering and erosion. The grains are carried by rivers, glaciers, the wind and ocean currents, and are deposited in layers, or strata. The majority of these detrital sediments are deposited in the sea, where many creatures and plants live. Rocks such as shale, clay, sandstone, breccia and conglomerate are detrital sediments. Structures within these sediments often give clues about the way in which they were deposited. These features enable geologists to work out the environment in which the sediments were formed. Such structures include ripple marks, dessication (or mud) cracks and cross-bedding. Whether the rocks have been upturned by folding can also be deduced by a study of these features.

Organic sediments are often made almost entirely of fossil fragments. Many limestones fall into this category, including shelly limestones, rich in mollusc or brachiopod shells, crinoids, or corals. Many of these rocks were initially shell banks that were cemented by lime mud that accumulated around the shells or other organic materials. Coal, which is formed from plant material, is another organic sediment.

The third group of sedimentary rocks are the chemically formed sediments. Some limestones, such as oolitic limestone, are in this group. Oolitic limestone is often rich in fossils and may contain the remains of molluscs and brachiopods. Rock salt, potash and gypsum are also chemically formed sediments, but these were formed in environments that were unfavourable for life, and therefore do not usually contain fossils.

▽ Dipping strata
Sedimentary rocks are frequently folded or tilted by movements in the Earth's crust. On this coastal wave-cut platform, the strata have been tilted so that they now slope, or dip, towards the land. A series of miniature escarpments and dip slopes has been created where the sea has eroded the softer shales which lie between the harder limestones. These strata are of Jurassic age and are rich in fossils.

△ Sedimentary strata
One of the main features that distinguishes sedimentary rocks from the other rock types is bedding or stratification. This coastal section clearly shows sandstone strata.

◁ Unconformity
Certain features of structural geology are well displayed by sedimentary rocks. Here, an unconformity separates an older series of steeply inclined slates from a younger series of horizontal limestones. The unconformity represents a time when erosion took place. Where an unconformity occurs, part of geological time is unrecorded.

FROM SEDIMENT TO ROCK

After sediment has been deposited it is subjected to a variety of processes, often in a very different environment from that in which deposition occurred. It undergoes compaction, during which any fluid in the spaces between the grains is squeezed out, and the grains may become more tightly packed. Another process known as cementation occurs as minerals form in the pore spaces. Quartz, calcite and iron oxides are common cements. These processes may have a profound effect on any fossils contained in the strata. Compaction may alter their shape and the chemical processes of cementation may remove the fossils or alter their chemical structure.

△ **Sandstone grains**
Many sedimentary rocks are composed of grains eroded from previously formed rocks. In this specimen of sandstone, the individual greyish quartz grains and a moderate amount of pinkish feldspar can be discerned.

▷ **Shale with ammonites**
Fine-grained sediments are often rich in fossil remains. This shale bedding plane is packed with crushed ammonites.

SEDIMENTARY STRATA AND UNCONFORMITY

Sedimentary strata, originally deposited in the sea and containing fossils of marine organisms (1), may be folded by movements in the Earth's crust (2). Erosion may remove some of the strata and younger sediments containing more recent fossils may then be deposited (3). The surface that separates the older and younger strata is known as an unconformity. The presence of fossils representing different time zones in the different strata is of great value in establishing the relative ages of rocks on either side of an unconformity.

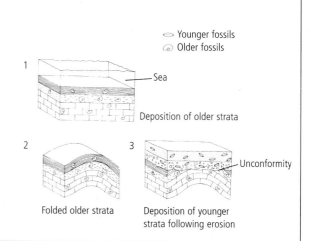

Younger fossils
Older fossils

Sea

Deposition of older strata

Unconformity

Folded older strata

Deposition of younger strata following erosion

◁ **Ripple marks and mud cracks**

The surface of sedimentary strata often gives clues as to the type of environment in which the rock was formed. These bedding planes display ripple marks and mud, or dessication cracks. Such features suggest a shallow-water environment that dried out from time to time.

▽ **Limestone detail**

This specimen is a piece of oolitic limestone that has been cut to show its composition. It contains numerous small rounded grains about 2mm (1/8in) in diameter. These are known as ooliths and are formed by the accretion of calcium carbonate around a nucleus. These sectioned fossils are mainly of molluscs. The largest fossil has an infilling of calcite crystals.

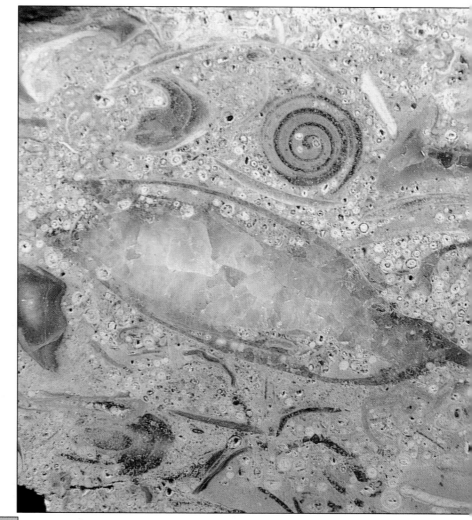

THE USES OF FOSSILS

Stratigraphers are geologists whose main concern is to determine the correct chronological sequence of the rocks of the Earth's crust and to interpret the events that resulted in their present arrangement. Sedimentary rocks that contain fossils have allowed a relative time scale to be established. Fossils have also been used to correlate strata over wide areas. The English canal engineer William Smith (1769–1839) was a pioneer in the stratigraphic use of fossils. He recognized that because certain strata contained particular fossils, he could link rocks from different areas by their fossils. In 1816 he published a book, *Strata Identified by Organized Fossils*, which set out the basic principles of stratigraphy, which are still followed today. His work as a canal engineer provided him with easy access to fresh rock sections. His geological maps, which appeared in 1815, were the first to show the outcrop of strata, and are remarkably accurate, even when compared with modern geological maps.

ZONE FOSSILS

Not all fossils are of equal use for stratigraphic work and the relative dating of rocks. The most valuable fossils for stratigraphers are those that occur in only a small vertical thickness of rock. This indicates that the species probably survived for only a short time. Such fossils are of great interest because the smaller the units of time that can be defined, the more precise is the time scale. Fossil species that belong to a rapidly evolving group usually existed for only a short time span. If that fossil species is geographically widespread, correlation of rocks in distant places may be possible. If such a species lived in the sea and was not controlled by the conditions on the sea bed, where the rocks were forming, it is likely to be of great assistance in the correlation of different rocks formed in varying environments.

Fossils used for stratigraphic work are called zone fossils. The time zone is the length of time that chosen species existed. This is, in effect, the smallest manageable unit of stratigraphy. Each zone is named after the representative fossil, and a number of zones are grouped into a stage. Stages are grouped into periods. Zones represented by graptolites in the Silurian period and Jurassic ammonite zones are less than one million years in duration.

Stratigraphic analysis is concerned with relative time. It is not possible to give absolute dates for the time scale unless radiometric dating of rocks has been carried out.

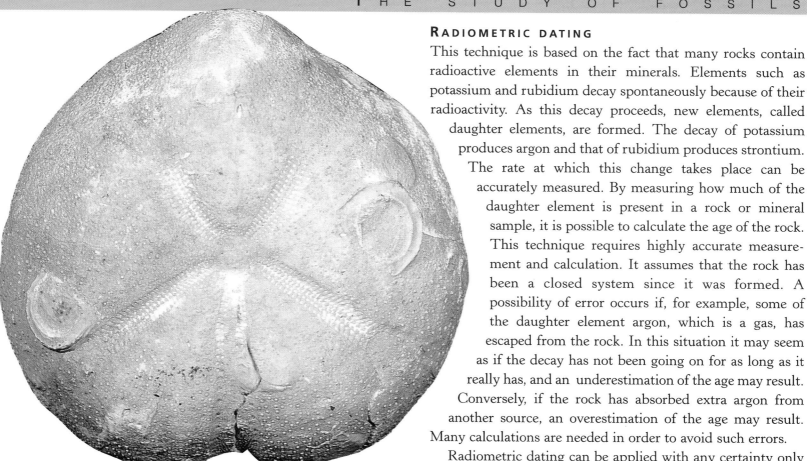

RADIOMETRIC DATING

This technique is based on the fact that many rocks contain radioactive elements in their minerals. Elements such as potassium and rubidium decay spontaneously because of their radioactivity. As this decay proceeds, new elements, called daughter elements, are formed. The decay of potassium produces argon and that of rubidium produces strontium.

The rate at which this change takes place can be accurately measured. By measuring how much of the daughter element is present in a rock or mineral sample, it is possible to calculate the age of the rock. This technique requires highly accurate measurement and calculation. It assumes that the rock has been a closed system since it was formed. A possibility of error occurs if, for example, some of the daughter element argon, which is a gas, has escaped from the rock. In this situation it may seem as if the decay has not been going on for as long as it really has, and an underestimation of the age may result. Conversely, if the rock has absorbed extra argon from another source, an overestimation of the age may result. Many calculations are needed in order to avoid such errors.

Radiometric dating can be applied with any certainty only

△ **Micraster**
Though not ideally suited to stratigraphic subdivision of strata, this echinoderm is used as a zone fossil in the Cretaceous rocks of Britain and Europe. It evolved rapidly into a number of species and each marks a different time zone.

▷ **Titanites**
Ammonites are possibly the best stratigraphic fossils. Even large genera such as this, which grew to over one metre (39in) in diameter, allow accurate correlation and relative dating of rocks. *Titanites* is of Upper Jurassic age.

◁ **Didymograptus**
Graptolites such as this are useful zone fossils in that they are very widespread and therefore allow correlation of strata over wide areas. *Didymograptus* is used for zoning the Ordovician system.

to rocks that have a definite point of formation involving the crystallization of minerals. It works best with igneous rocks, which also contain plenty of the right elements. Many metamorphic rocks are also suitable, but sedimentary, fossil-bearing rocks are not good subjects for this technique because they are often formed from material derived from older rocks. The mineral glauconite, which occurs in some sandstones and may give them a greenish colour, can provide good radiometric results. The best way to provide absolute dates for fossil-bearing strata is to use those which are interbedded with lava flows. Radiometric dates can be obtained for the minerals in

△ **Graptolites**
These organisms were probably planktonic and drifted over the oceans. Their remains are found in deep-sea sediments.

▷ **Reef limestone**
This small specimen from a limestone reef shows many of the characteristics of that shallow-water environment. The net-like fossil is of a bryozoan, one of the organisms which, because of its structure, helped to bind the lime mud together. The rock lacks stratification and contains other fossils including a goniatite.

▽ **Coral environments**
Modern corals require special ecological conditions, such as clear, warm sea water. By analogy, fossil corals may have needed a similar habitat. The presence of fossil corals therefore enables us to guess at the environmental conditions that prevailed in the past.

the lava flows, thus allowing the age of the fossil-bearing strata to be determined.

FOSSILS AND PAST ENVIRONMENTS

Palaeoecology is the science concerned with the study of ancient environments. Comparisons between fossils and modern organisms are essential for this work, as well as detailed investigation of the sedimentary rock in which the fossils occur. The principle of uniformitarianism underlies palaeoecological investigation. This principle, which has many geological applications, was first defined by Charles Lyell (1797-1875). He coined the phrase 'the present is the key to the past', which is a brief summary of the principle. Uniformitarianism suggests that the processes we observe on the Earth today also took place during the past, and that rocks can therefore be interpreted accordingly. Through application of our knowledge of current geological and biological processes we can make informed guesses about the environmental conditions that existed in the past.

On the whole this approach works well. However, problems arise in the study of older rocks. The further we move from our place of reference (here and now), the less reliable uniformitarianism becomes. Studying the ecology of the past through rocks is a little like travelling into space. The further we travel from what we know, the less certain we are that our assumptions hold good. We know that in the distant past the Earth had a very different atmosphere and the oceans had a different chemistry. In the Pre-Cambrian era the Earth was hotter than it is today and the conditions that formed some rocks then may never occur again.

Most fossils are of sea creatures and plants. Marine environments are thus the easiest to reconstruct. The conditions of depth, temperature, aeration, light and salinity all influence the development of organisms. Some creatures are exclusively marine. Echinoderms and brachiopods only live in the sea. Corals are another exclusively marine group, and many genera require warm, clear sea water. A number of gastropods and bivalve molluscs are found in fresh water and some require brackish conditions where salt and fresh water mix.

Plant fossils are very useful as climatic indicators. Even preserved pollen grains or spores can be used to provide information about the climate that existed in the past. Because plants are so sensitive to climatic conditions, their fossils have been used to prove that continental drift occurred (see page 35). The plants found in the Carboniferous rocks of North America and Europe are not unlike those found today at low latitudes. Similarly, the pollen found in glacial sediments can be used to work out accurately the ebb and flow of the glaciers and ice sheets during the last two million years.

GEOLOGICAL TIME SCALE

MYA*	PERIODS		ERAS	EONS	MYA*
0.01	RECENT	QUATERNARY			
2	PLEISTOCENE				
5	PLIOCENE				
22.5	MIOCENE	TERTIARY	CENOZOIC		
37.5	OLIGOCENE				
53.5	EOCENE			PHANERZOIC	
65	PALAEOCENE				
136		CRETACEOUS			
190		JURASSIC	MEZOZOIC		
225		TRIASSIC			
280		PERMIAN			
345		CARBONIFEROUS	UPPER PALAEOZOIC		
395		DEVONIAN			
440		SILURIAN			
500		ORDOVICIAN	LOWER PALAEOZOIC		
600		CAMBRIAN			600
			PRE-CAMBRIAN	PROTEROZOIC	2500
				ARCHAEAN	
4600					4600

*MYA = Millions of years ago

LOOKING FOR FOSSILS

There are three stages to a well-organized fossil-hunting expedition. Though exciting finds can be, and often have been, made by chance, the better prepared you are the greater the likelihood of success. Research is the first stage. This may involve referring to geological maps, journals, local field guides, and other books.

Geological maps show where the stratum in which you hope to search occurs on the ground. Such maps are designed to show the outcrop of strata, but this is not the same as the exposure. Outcrops are the area over which a stratum exists. This is often obscured by roads, buildings, playing fields and superficial deposits such as soil, river alluvium and glacial debris. Exposure is where the rock is open to the sky, and it is exposure that is important for the amateur fossil-hunter.

Read the map carefully and look for places where the stratum under consideration is cut by a river or where it occurs on a steep slope or sea cliff. There is a good chance that in such places the rock will be exposed, making collecting possible. There are many man-made as well as natural exposures. These include road and disused rail cuttings, excavations for foundations and pipe-lines, and quarries. Good geological guide books provide accurate map references for fossil-rich localities. The problem then is that many geologists will have collected specimens there before you.

COLLECTING SPECIMENS

The second stage is to go into the field. It is essential to collect only in moderation and also to resist the inappropriate use of a geological hammer. This piece of equipment is useful for breaking up loose blocks as at the foot of a scree slope, or on a beach, but it should not be used for active quarrying of the rock face. Take plenty of collecting bags and packing material for protecting specimens in transit. Though it is often forgotten and many regard it as a tedious part of the activity, it is important to take notes and to make sketches of the location. The fossils you have collected will have much greater scientific significance if their location is properly documented. Record the name of the site and, if possible, the place of the exposure from which the material came. Make a particular note if you are lucky enough to find a number of fossils in the same stratum. A camera is an essential piece of field equipment for recording details of the exposure and 'collecting' specimens that may be too large to take away.

PRECAUTIONS

In all situations, especially where rock faces are encountered, safety precautions, such as the wearing of a hard hat, must be taken. It is also essential to obtain permission before going onto land and collecting material. Rocks and fossils are the land-owner's property, and most land is privately owned.

◁ **Limestone gorge**
Fossils may be found where weathering and erosion have revealed rock strata. Limestones are often rich in fossils and the slopes of valleys such as this may have loose scree and rock fragments, from which fossils can be recovered.

◁ Limestone quarry
Man-made exposures such as quarries, road and rail cuttings, and the excavations for the foundations of buildings may provide rich sites for fossil-hunters. Permission must be sought before collecting in such locations; even abandoned quarries are private property.

▽ Coastal cliffs
The coast provides many of the best rock exposures for finding fossils. In this example, the cliffs and wave-cut platform are made up of Jurassic shales and sandstones. These strata contain numerous fossils of molluscs and plants, and occasional vertebrates.

▷ **Waterfalls**
River cliffs and waterfalls create exposures of bare rock that may reveal fossils. Fallen blocks in a gorge and below waterfalls provide easy collecting, but to be of scientific value the specimens must be collected from the stratum in which they occur, or be certainly associated with it.

IDENTIFYING AND CARING FOR YOUR FINDS

Finally comes the identification and curating stage. Identification may have been possible in the field, but you are likely to have more reference material at home or available through a library. Identification of a fossil specimen to generic level is a good standard to reach, but it may be possible to give species names to some items.

When you return home, you may need to remove loose rock debris and other extraneous matter from your finds. This is often a delicate job and may require special tools and techniques. If in any doubt about cleaning specimens, leave them, and seek expert help and advice from a local museum or the palaeontology department of a university.

A number of everyday tools may be of use. Paint brushes of various thicknesses and stiffness are invaluable for removing small particles of sediment from delicate fossils. Knife blades, fine screwdrivers, bradawls and other tools may help to remove tougher material. Various liquids can be used to dissolve rock matrix from fossils, but great care has to be taken not to damage the fossils or to harm your hands and eyes. Distilled water does not harm fossils and may be used to wash away loose material. Dilute hydrochloric acid will dissolve limestone, but will also do irreparable damage to calcareous (chalk-based) fossils. If you are certain that fossils embedded in limestone are made of non-calcareous minerals, you can carefully remove the limestone with dilute hydrochloric acid, but always have plenty of water close at hand to wash this away in case the process appears to be damaging the specimen.

When you have prepared the specimens, you need to decide whether to store or display your finds. Fossils are best displayed behind glass, as specimens on open shelves gather dust in their cavities and may be damaged. Glass cabinets are available in various styles and sizes. A collection of fossils may be of considerable weight and the cabinet must be able to withstand this.

If you decide to store your finds out of sight, office type, metal filing cabinets are a good option. They are strong and are available with drawers of different depths. It is important to separate individual specimens within the cabinet drawer to prevent them from rubbing together, which may cause damage. The best method is to use individual card trays for each item. Place a label with the name, location, and other details of the fossil in the base of each tray. You may also mark the specimens with an individual reference number by writing on a small spot of white paint or correcting fluid. The marking should, of course, be on the rock matrix or a part of the specimen that is of no great consequence. This reference number can also be recorded in a card index or on computer.

△ **Storage of specimens**
Ammonites and bivalve molluscs are housed in a drawer in individual cardboard trays to keep them from rubbing against each other. Each tray has a label with the name of the specimen, location and other details.

CHAPTER 2 PLANTS

Evidence from Pre-Cambrian rocks suggests that the first living cells developed about 4,000 million years ago. At this time, the Earth's atmosphere contained no oxygen. Some of the earliest fossil remains are of lime mounds secreted by blue-green algae. These are called stromatolites, and represent the first plants. The fossil record of plants during the Pre-Cambrian era is not extensive, although the ancestors of the diverse flora of the subsequent Lower Palaeozoic era must have developed by then.

These early, primitive algae had a profound effect. Most importantly, they produced oxygen, which accumulated in the atmosphere. Green plants have continued to fulfil this function ever since. The oldest vascular plants (plants with veins) are found in rocks from the Silurian period. Such plants transport water through the entire plant structure by means of special xylem cells in their veins. Spores and other microscopic parts of these plants have been found in Silurian strata in Wales. Plants with rigid xylem in their stems were able to stand upright and lived in damp swampy conditions. *Cooksonia* (illustrated on page 30) is a representative of these early plants which relied on a damp environment for their spore-based reproductive system.

It is not until the Devonian period that large numbers of plant fossils were formed. A link between water and land plants has been discovered in Aberdeenshire in Scotland, where plant materials are very well preserved in chert (a siliceous nodular material not uncommon in certain sedimentary rocks). This chert contains fossilized remains of *Rhynia*, a plant genus thought to have grown in boggy conditions. *Rhynia* is distinguished by its spore-bearing structures and thin stems without leaves. These stems are of woody tissue and the waxy cuticle covering their outer surface is a feature that suggests that it may also have flourished on land. Such plants were never very tall, reaching about one metre (39in) in height.

THE GYMNOSPERMS

During the Devonian period the gymnosperms – a group that includes pines, firs, cycads and junipers – also developed. This was an important advance because these plants use seeds instead of spores for reproduction. During the Carboniferous period luxuriant forests with tall plants reaching a height of 30 metres (100ft) developed in many parts of the world. The remains of these forests are preserved as coal, and the energy released when this fuel is burnt is energy from the sun that was originally trapped by the plants of the Carboniferous period. The most important plant group at this time was the lycopods (clubmosses), such as *Lepidodendron*. These grew to great size, with a stem diameter of over one metre (39in). Great horsetails,

◁△ **Williamsonia**

A leaf preserved as a thin carbon film in Middle Jurassic sandstone.

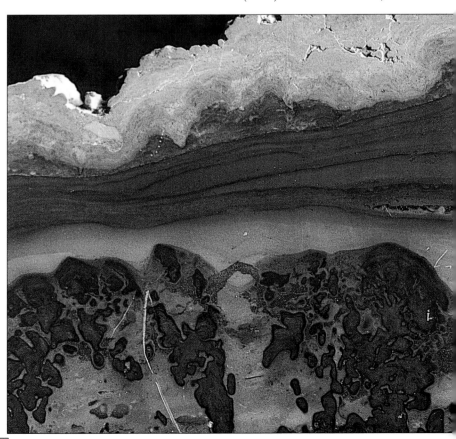

◁ **Solenopora**

This form of *Solenopora* ranges in age from Ordovician to Jurassic, worldwide. This specimen from the Ordovician sediments of southern Norway, is small, the field of view being only about 40mm (1⁵/₈in) across. It takes a very different form from *S. jurassica*. It has a slender, tube-shaped, calcareous structure. These tubes are porous and have Y-shaped branches. Such algae are common in reef deposits, and their skeletons, together with those of bryozoans, help to bind the finer grained reef sediments. Because they are built of calcite these algal structures are readily fossilized.

▽ **Landscape marble**

This specimen, from rocks of Triassic age in southern England, shows algal structures that developed as mounds growing on mud flats. It is about 100mm (4in) long. The mounds in this type of fossil are thought to have been secreted by algae. The sediment surrounding them is muddy limestone. Originally these structures were believed to have been formed inorganically, but recent research and comparisons with the stromatolite mounds in Shark Bay, Western Australia, suggest that they were formed by algae in a lagoon, or land-locked basin. Lens-shaped masses of small gastropods are often found with this deposit. Possibly these snails fed on the algae. This specimen illustrates the 'landscape' description of the rock well.

△ **Solenopora jurassica**

Solenopora has a wide distribution in rocks ranging from Lower Palaeozoic to Recent in age. It is the calcareous structure secreted by an alga. This specimen, found in Gloucestershire, UK, is about 120mm (4³/₄in) in height and dates from the Middle Jurassic period. The pink and white banding may be original or may have been created by the movement of water through the deposits after its formation. The rock in which this type of *Solenopora* is found is referred to as 'beetroot stone' because of the colour. Detailed examination of the fossils has shown that the alternating colour bands correspond closely with the variations in the structure of the algal deposits. The layers consist of alternating bands of porous and less porous material. Pigment carried by downward-moving waters could have become concentrated in the less porous layers.

the Equisetales, also flourished. This genus includes plants such as *Calamites*. Another important group, frequently found as delicate carbonized fossils, are the tree-sized seed ferns including *Alethopteris* and *Neuropteris*. These 'coal forests' spread widely over much of what is now North America, Europe and Asia. Towards the end of the Palaeozoic era and during the early part of the Mesozoic much of the area previously covered by the swamp forests of the Carboniferous period became arid and unable to support such luxuriant plant life. In this later period, the ferns, clubmosses and horsetails are represented by fewer genera, but in some areas conifers were abundant.

The seed fern *Glossopteris* flourished during the Permian period. Fossils of this bushy plant are found in Antarctica, India, South Africa and South America, suggesting that these continents were joined when the plant lived, and thereby providing evidence to support the theory of continental drift (see page 35). In the Triassic period the ginkgos and cycads emerged, which continued to evolve during the Jurassic period. The ginkgos are deciduous trees, that are still represented by one genus today, a native of China. The cycads are palm-like, and have rough stems and pinnate leaves. At this time, the conifers became a dominant plant group. These are characterized by their resinous secretions and great longevity.

▽▷ *Stromatolites*

Stromatolites vary in size from about one metre (39in) in diameter to a few centimetres. The single specimen shown here is 20mm (³/₄in) across its base. The double mound (below) is 100mm (4in) across. The occurrence of fossils such as these indicates an environment lacking in oxygen. The double-mound specimen shows the typical curving layers of lime secreted by the algae. This example is from the Jurassic period. Stromatolites are easily fossilized, being virtually rock as they form. Many Pre-Cambrian limestones contain a high percentage of stromatolite material.

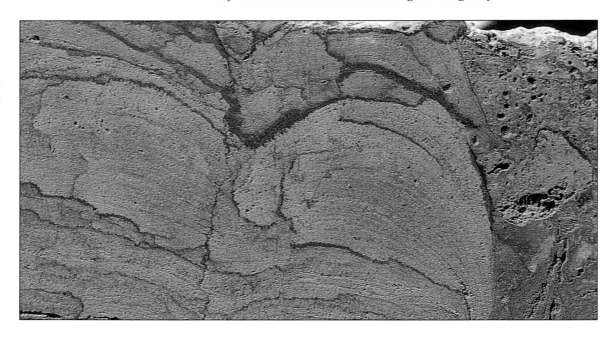

THE ANGIOSPERMS

Flowering plants, the angiosperms, made their debut late in the Mesozoic era, adding colour to the Earth's vegetation. Flowers were an important development because they permitted cross-pollination, which gives plants greater adaptability by allowing new combinations of genes to occur. Insects, which had evolved early in the Palaeozoic era, took advantage of flowering plants as they could feed on both pollen and nectar. Indeed the evolution of both groups took place together. Many plants developed intricate mechanisms for making themselves attractive to insects that would pollinate the flowers. During the Tertiary era the world's vegetation was very similar to that of today, and detailed reconstruction of the climate can be attempted by studying fossil floras. This work is of great value in the study of the Quaternary ice age. The fluctuations in climate associated with ice advances and retreat can be based on the evidence of fossil plant materials, especially pollen.

THE FORMATION OF PLANT FOSSILS

Remains of plants are not commonly preserved as fossils. Plants – particularly those that grow on land – decay rapidly after they die. Those living under water stand a better chance of preservation, especially if they are rapidly covered with sand or mud. Possibly the most favourable conditions are when plant remains are deposited in anaerobic (oxygen-lacking) conditions, because the bacterial action that causes decay is then severely limited.

The most common plant fossils are thin, delicate carbon films on the rock surface (bedding plane). These consist of the plant carbon, all the other original material having been removed. In some cases, plant material may be silicified, as in the case of the Rhynie chert in Aberdeenshire. Replacement of the plant material with calcite and other minerals sometimes occurs – for example, in the nodular coal balls of the Carboniferous age. Usually plant fossils are the incomplete remains of plants – showing only the leaves, roots, seeds or branches. For this reason, the different fossilized parts of the same plant have often been given different scientific names.

STROMATOLITE FORMATION

Stromatolites are the mounds of calcite secreted by types of blue-green algae. Some of the earliest fossils are of these structures, which date far back into the Pre-Cambrian era. Some stromatolites are over 3,500 million years old. They are found in Europe, North America and Africa.

Stromatolites are still being formed in some parts of the world today, notably in Western Australia. In these areas, the hypersaline (highly salty) environment is too harsh for many organisms. However, the algae (cyanobacteria) that secrete the limey stromatolite mounds, flourish in these conditions. These organisms were abundant in the Pre-Cambrian era; It is because these organisms produced oxygen that this vital gas became relatively abundant in the atmosphere for the first time. When the original stromatolites flourished, this oxygen was used up in the conversion of iron into iron oxide minerals, such as hematite. It was probably only after much of the iron available had been transformed in this way that oxygen began to be released into the sea and then into the air.

Because stromatolites are the product of the action of blue-green algae and anaerobic bacteria, once oxygen became a significant component of the atmosphere, they became restricted to habitats lacking in oxygen. Today stromatolites occur only in very specialized environments.

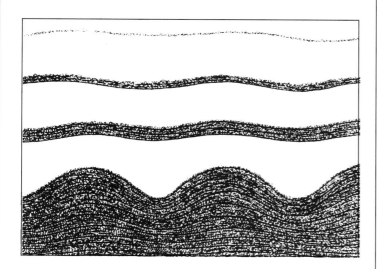

The mat of algae secretes a layer of lime which traps some of the seawater sediment. As the structure develops, it takes on a mounded form. The word stromatolite is from the Greek 'stroma' meaning a bed.

△ **Stromatolite**
These heaped layers of calcite are set in a brownish muddy matrix. They were photographed on a sea cliff of Torridonian strata in Northwest Scotland. Only about 50mm (2in) across, they form a thin limestone deposit, which can be traced for a number of miles. Their structure is typical of calcite secretions by algae. In effect, they are miniature stromatolites and are, therefore, among the oldest British fossils.

▽ Cooksonia

This is a fossil of the first vascular plant genus to occur in the fossil record. These plants have water-transporting cells made of xylem. The rigid vascular structure also helped the plant to stand upright. *Cooksonia* reproduced by means of spores carried in a capsule on the tip of the stem. There were no leaves. Roots helped to secure it in the swampy mud in which it lived. Spores develop only where the conditions are very moist. After they have settled on the surface of the wet sediment, a green bloom of tissue develops. This is called the prothallus and contains both male and female structures. Modern plants such as ferns reproduce in this way. *Cooksonia* belongs to a group called the Psilophytes. The genus is found in many areas, including North America, Europe, Africa, Asia and Antarctica. This specimen, from Scottish rocks of Devonian age, is about 70mm (2³/₄ in) across.

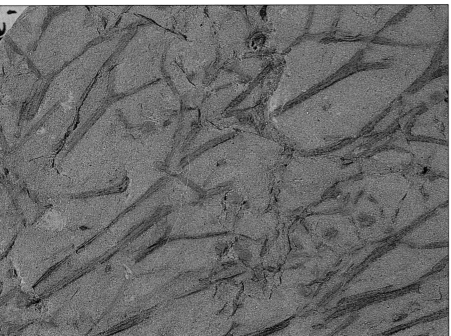

△ Parka

This form of algae was composed of a circular thallus – well preserved in this specimen – and many smaller rounded internal structures. It reproduced by means of spores, which were coated with a tough cuticle. *Parka* was one of the first plants to become adapted to living on land with its structure out of water. It was not large, this example is typical at about 30mm (1¹/₈ in) in diameter. *Parka* is found in rocks of Silurian and Devonian age in many parts of the world. This specimen was found in Devonian strata in Angus, Scotland.

▷ Eupecopteris

Plant fossils are sometimes preserved in nodular masses that form within the layers of sediment containing them. Such nodules sometimes preserve the remains in three-dimensional form. In this example the nodule is of brownish ironstone, and much of the original plant detail can be seen. It is a typical member of the Pteridosperm (seed fern) group. These have woody stems and annual growth rings. This 60mm (2³/₈in) long specimen consists of a single leaf with a straight central axis and numerous leaflets. It is from the Upper Carboniferous rocks of Mazon Creek, Illinois, USA. Plants of this genus are common in rocks of this age in North America, Europe and Asia.

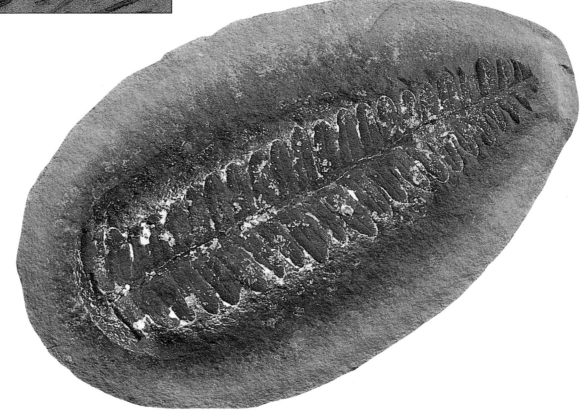

◁ **Mariopteris**
This genus belongs to the true ferns, the pteridophytes. They reproduce by means of spores and therefore need to live in a damp environment. Each leaf has a central stem with offset leaflets. These fossils are common in the coal-bearing strata from the Upper Carboniferous period in many regions, especially North America and Europe. This specimen is about 55mm (2$\frac{1}{8}$ in) long.

▽ **Sphenopteris**
This is a typical pteridosperm (seed fern) plant but there is little evidence of its structure apart from its delicate fossilized leaves. It is thought to have been a shrubby plant that lived in marshy conditions. The leaves have slightly toothed margins. *Sphenopteris* lived all over the world during the Permian and Carboniferous periods. This specimen is 60mm (2$\frac{3}{8}$ in) long.

COAL FORMATION

Coal still provides much of the world's energy. Most of the usable coal was formed during the Carboniferous period from the accumulation of forest peat. Before this time, plants were not sufficiently developed to create the great thicknesses of peat required for coal formation. It is not fully understood why most of the usable coal was formed in a period of only 75 million years at the end of the Palaeozoic era. At this time there was a supercontinent called Gondwanaland (see Continental drift, page 35) upon which warm-temperate and sub-tropical coal forests flourished. Here high rainfall promoted rapid growth. Much of the forest vegetation grew near to sea level, often in the region of vast deltas. In such a situation even small changes of sea level have a marked effect, and the forest vegetation was frequently inundated with sea water. The coal seams are thus interbedded with marine and non-marine sedimentary rocks related to sea-level changes.

FROM PEAT TO COAL

Further changes were needed to convert the layers of peat into good quality coal. The peat was compressed as layers of sediment were built up over it. Heat formation in the peat layers was another important factor. Peat contains much volatile material (such as water) and this was driven out by an increase in temperature, thus increasing the percentage of carbon in the deposits. Peat (with only about 30 per cent fixed carbon) is much used as a fuel, as is lignite (brown coal with up to 40 per cent fixed carbon). Bituminous coal has over 75 per cent fixed carbon. The best quality coal is anthracite with over 80 per cent fixed carbon. The oldest coals, which have been subjected to most change, tend to have the highest carbon content.

△▽ *Lepidodendron*

These fossils are of parts of a giant lycopod (clubmoss), which was common during the Carboniferous period. It grew to a height of over 30m (100ft). Its thick stem was covered in non-woody outer tissue. Over a hundred species have been described, subdivided on the basis of the marks on the stem where leaves have broken off. The darker fossil has diamond-shaped leaf scars. It is thought that these plants grew to their great height in only a few years because of the warm climate in which they lived.

As is common with many fossil plants, *Lepidodendron* was often fragmented before fossilization, and the various parts of the plant have been given different scientific names. The horizontally growing roots are called *Stigmaria* and leaves *Sigillaria*. The other specimen illustrated shows a leafy branch. *Lepidodendron* is found in Upper Carboniferous rocks in many parts of the world, including Europe, North Africa and Asia.

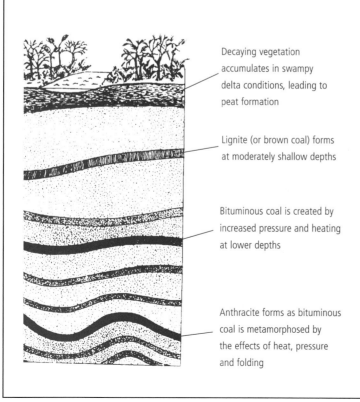

Decaying vegetation accumulates in swampy delta conditions, leading to peat formation

Lignite (or brown coal) forms at moderately shallow depths

Bituminous coal is created by increased pressure and heating at lower depths

Anthracite forms as bituminous coal is metamorphosed by the effects of heat, pressure and folding

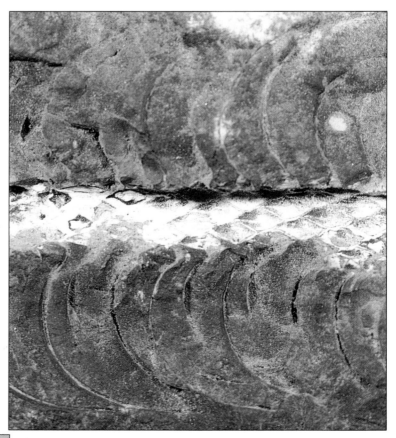

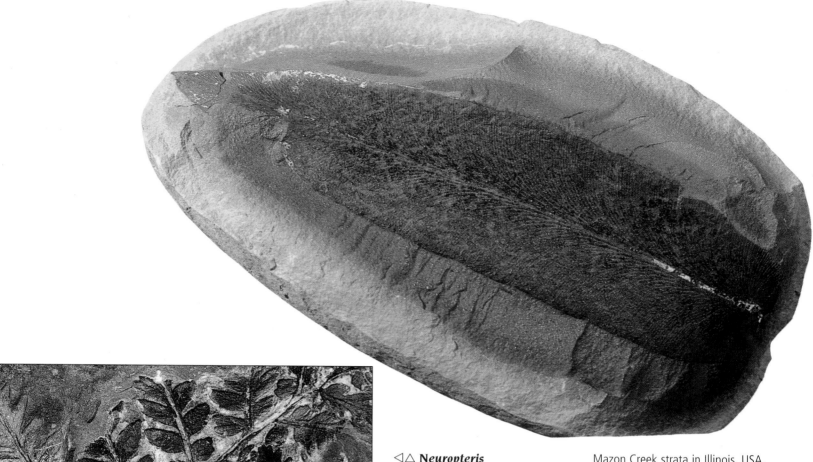

◁△ *Neuropteris*

Neuropteris is a genus of pteridosperms. Its oval leaflets are commonly found separated from the main stem. It occurs in strata of Carboniferous age in North America and Europe. The specimen (left) is shown preserved as a carbon film on a shale bedding plane. The other (above) is in an ironstone nodule. This nodule is from the famous Mazon Creek strata in Illinois, USA. As well as perfectly preserved plant fossils, nodules from this site contain various small water creatures such as worms and crustaceans. These deposits give much greater insight into the ecology of the Upper Carboniferous forests than most fossil assemblages of that age.

◁ *Annularia*

This is the scientific name for the leaves of the horsetail genus *Calamites. Annularia* consists of delicate rosettes of leaflets. The individual leaves can be oval or lance-shaped, depending on the species. Different species also vary in the spacing of the leaf whorls and the leaf length. *Annularia* bore spore cases on the tips of its branches. The genus occurs in Carboniferous strata in North America, Europe and Asia. This specimen is from Radstock, Somerset, UK.

▷ *Glossopteris*

This is a genus of bushy plants classified with the pteridosperms (seed ferns). The photograph shows a number of the leaves that have been flattened on a bedding plane. They are characterized by thin veins that curve out delicately from the central leaf axis. The mature plant grew to about 6m (19¹/₂ ft) in height and flourished during the Permian and Triassic periods. The generic name *Glossopteris* is used to describe much of the plant life that existed in specific parts of the world during the late Palaeozoic and early Mesozoic eras. *Glossopteris* fossils are found in southern South America, southern Africa, India,

Madagascar, much of Australia, New Zealand and Antarctica. This specimen of *Glossopteris* was collected at Adamstown in Australia.

◁ *Ginkgo*

This genus is today represented by a single species native in China. The genus – a cycad – is a deciduous plant. The male and female reproductive parts are on separate plants. The male tree bears cones with sporangia, the female has ovules. The leaves are typically triangular in shape with a deeply cut outer edge. Identification of fossils is made difficult by the fact that a single tree can bear a variety of leaf shapes. The leaves shown are about 30mm (1¹/₈ in) across. The mature tree can be 30m (100ft) high. The genus *Ginkgo* is found all

over the world in strata dating from the Permian period. The pictured example dates from the Middle Jurassic period and was found in North Yorkshire, UK.

▷ *Williamsonia*

This fossil is of a common genus belonging to the primitive cycadophytes. The most important fossil groups of this class are the cycads, which have living representatives, and the bennettitales, which are extinct. *Williamsonia* belongs to the latter group. A feature of this genus is that it bore hermaphroditic flowers.

The specimen shows the characteristic pinnate leaves, which here are about 30mm (1¹/₈in) long. The history of the bennettitales begins in the Permian period. They became extinct in the early part of the Tertiary era. *Williamsonia* is found worldwide in strata of Jurassic age. The specimen is of Middle Jurassic age.

Alfred Wegener (1880-1930) was the first scientist to present a strong case, based on all types of evidence including fossils, for continental drift. He argued that the now distant areas which contain fossils of the *Glossopteris* flora must have been joined together at the time when the flora was alive. Wegener was a meteorologist, not a geologist, and his revolutionary ideas and evidence brought together in his book *The Origin of Continents and Oceans* in 1924 were strongly opposed by the geological establishment. His ideas produced bitter argument. The established line was that land bridges must have existed between the continents along which flora and fauna could spread. These have now sunk without trace. His ideas, as is not uncommonly the way with science, were in fact far more elegant and straightforward and the weight of his evidence was overpowering. Today it is firmly believed that the southern continents where *Glossopteris* is found were joined when the plants grew, and the continents have since that time drifted apart.

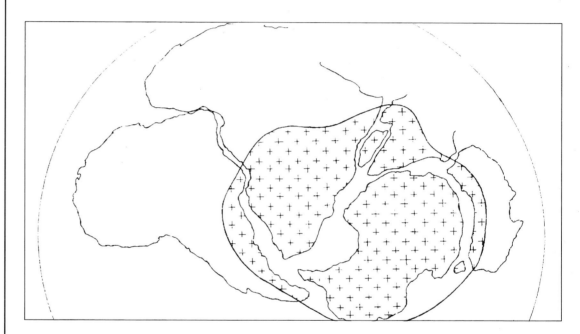

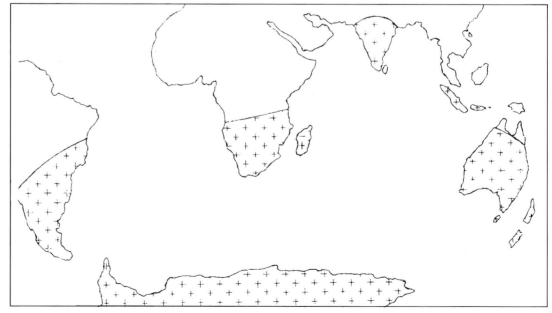

Top - Distribution of *Glossopteris* in Permian and Triassic times.

Above - Distribution of *Glossopteris* fossils today.

△ *Calamites*

This specimen is of part of the stem of a large horsetail plant which is typically jointed and also has longitudinal markings, very like the smaller modern horsetails. *Calamites* was a tree-sized horsetail growing to a height of about 30m (100ft). The centre of the stem was made of pith (soft tissue) which decayed quickly on death. Therefore the fossils, as in the pictured specimen, are often of hollow stems infilled with sediment.

The specimen shown is preserved in sandstone that contains small glittering flakes of mica. All that remains of the original plant tissue is the thin film of carbon on the surface of the fossil. *Calamites* occurs in strata of the Carboniferous and Permian periods in North America, Europe and Asia.

▷ *Coniopteris*

This is a genus of ferns that grew in damp conditions during the Mesozoic era. The fossil is preserved as a carbon film on a bedding plane. *Coniopteris* is characterized by a central stem with leaflets growing in a conical shape. The upper margins of the leaflets are slightly indented. Each section of fern pictured is about 20mm (³/₄in) long. *Coniopteris* has a wide distribution, occurring in Mesozoic rocks in North America, Europe, India, Japan and other parts of Asia.

▽ *Salix*

Plants of this genus within the angiosperm group probably lived in damp conditions as do modern members of the same genus – the willows. The leaf shown here, which is 30mm (1¹/₄in) long, has the typical veining and central axis of many modern tree leaves. These leaves are preserved as fossils only if they are buried rapidly in fine-grained sediment. *Salix* fossils are found in strata of Tertiary age to Recent. This specimen is from the Eocene rocks of Colorado, USA.

▷ *Acer*

This delicate fossil leaf is of the genus that includes modern maples and sycamores. It belongs to the angiosperm group. The male and female parts of the *Acer* genus are carried on the same plant, commonly within a single flower. A characteristic feature, which can be seen in this specimen, is the leaf veining. This genus evolved during the Tertiary period and has worldwide distribution. The pictured specimen was found in Miocene strata near Paris, France.

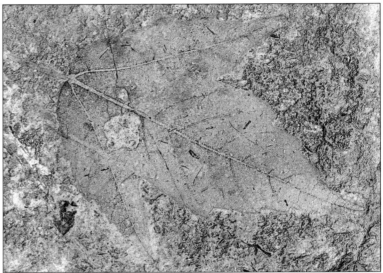

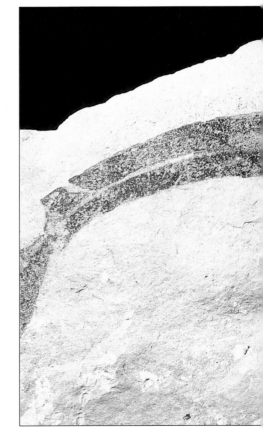

F O S S I L   P O L L E N

Because plant species are quite particular about the climatic conditions they will tolerate, fossil plant materials are good indicators of past climates. As well as leaves and stems, pollen and spores become fossilized. One important use for fossil pollen analysis is in the reconstruction of the climatic conditions during the most recent ice age. Pollen was carried by the wind and accumulated in peat and lake sediments during interglacial periods. The type of pollen found at different levels in the sediments varies according to the climate of the time. Many of the species whose pollen has been found are alive today and so the exact conditions they require are well documented. *Salix herbacea* and other cold climate plants, such as *Dryas octopetala*, are found in Northern Europe in sediments dating from the end of the last ice age, about 10,000 years ago. Later sediments contain pollen from species including *Alnus*, *Quercus* and *Betula*, suggesting the onset of milder conditions.

▽ Myrica
The bog myrtle is known for its spicy fragrance. It grows today in cool-temperate climates, as a bushy plant with woody stems, rarely reaching more than a metre (39in) in height. This leaf from Oligocene rocks in Provence, France, is very similar to those of the modern bog myrtle. This leaf is about 40mm (1⅝in) long.

▷ Quercus
Quercus is a deciduous genus that developed during the Tertiary period. This elongated leaf fossil is from Oligocene rocks in the Paris Basin, France. It is 25mm (1in) long. Modern oaks belong to the *Quercus* genus.

△ Betula
Modern birch trees belong to this genus of angiosperms. This oval leaf has veins that branch from the central axis. Networks of irregularly shaped smaller veins subdivide the spaces between the main veins. Trees of this genus developed during the Tertiary period and are still common today. This specimen is preserved only as a delicate impression in the sediment. None of the original carbon of the plant tissue is present. It is from the Eocene strata of Colorado, USA and is 65mm (2½in) long.

3 CORALS & SPONGES

This chapter includes fossils of the Anthozoa class in the phylum Cnidaria and fossil sponges of the phylum Porifera. There are three important groups of corals that are commonly found as fossils – Tabulata, Rugosa and Zoantharia. The latter includes the order Scleractinia – the hexacorals, which are important as fossils from Triassic times onwards. The Rugosa and Tabulata are extinct but were numerous in the past, especially during the Palaeozoic era. Fossils of organisms from these groups have been found in rocks ranging in age from Ordovician to Permian.

CORAL STRUCTURES

The basic coral structure consists of a tube – a cone-shaped corallite – made of calcite. In the upper surface there is a small depression called a calice, in which the coral-secreting polyp lived. In some corals the corallite may be joined to others to form a colony, with the corallite walls touching or even shared. Other corals are solitary though many individuals may live in the same area of the sea bed. Tabulata corals are invariably colonial, whereas the Rugosa and Scleractinia may be either solitary or colonial.

The structure of the corallite can vary considerably. It may be a very simple tube with smooth outside surfaces and few internal structures. Usually even the simplest corals, the tabulates, have horizontal plates, called tabulae, that divide the corallite into layers. Vertical calcite sheets (or septa) arranged in a radiating fashion are found in many genera. These septa are like the spokes in a wheel when the coral is seen in cross-section. Through the centre of the corallite there is sometimes an axial column from which septa may radiate. The number and arrangement of the septa is important for identification. Many scleractinian corals have their septa arranged in groups of six; the rugose corals tend to have theirs in groups of four. The corallite wall is often thickened and strengthened by delicate structures of calcite. When seen in cross-section they have the appearance of a spider's web.

△ **Favosites**
This coral belongs to the tabulate group. It has a rounded outline which contains many small, closely packed, colonial corallites. These have a polygonal cross-section and may have very short spiny septa. The thecae (structures enclosing the coral polyp) are well-developed, dividing the corallites horizontally. The thecal walls are porous.

The overall coral mass which can grow to about 150 mm (6 in) in diameter is sometimes referred to as a 'honeycomb' coral. It flourished in a shallow marine environment and is found in strata ranging from the Ordovician to the Middle Devonian periods. The pictured specimen was found in Silurian limestone in Shropshire, UK.

◁△ **Thysanophyllum**
This fossil colonial coral is shown in close-up. Even in this rather weathered specimen many of the characteristic features of Palaeozoic

corals are visible. The septa, which radiate from the centre, have been etched by weathering and in the middle of each corallite the thin columella can be discerned.

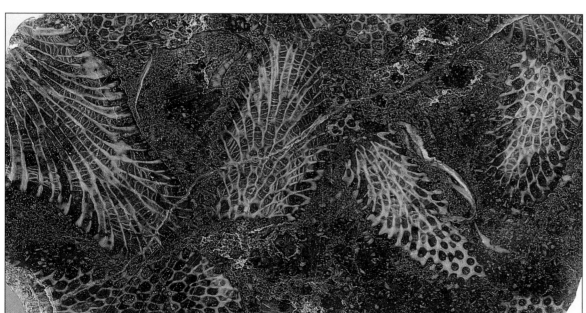

CORAL ANATOMY

- Thecal wall
- Tabula
- Axial column
- Dissepiments
- Septum

This diagram shows the structure of a typical solitary coral. Soft tissues are not shown.

△ *Halysites*

This tabulate coral is easily recognized by its sinuous chain-like structure in which the individual corallites are linked on two or three sides. These corallites are ovoid or circular in cross-section and are internally divided by horizontal tabulae. There are no septa. *Halysites* is a common reef-building coral from shallow marine rocks mainly from the Silurian period. It is found in many sites around the world. The individual corallites are 2mm (¹⁄₁₆in) across. This specimen is from the Silurian limestones of Wenlock Edge, Shropshire, UK.

◁ *Thamnopora*

This colonial, tabulate genus grew in off-reef situations during the Devonian period. Its branching structures grew to about 100mm (4in) in diameter. It is associated in the Devonian limestones with other corals and Brachiopods. This polished specimen clearly shows the internal tabulae. Short spinose septa are also visible. The specimen shown is from Torquay, UK.

▷ **Dibunophyllum**

This specimen has been cut to show the delicate internal detail. A solitary, rugose coral, it has the complex internal structure characteristic of this group. There are numerous radiating septa which, in this example, can be seen as thin, pale lines in both cross-section and longitudinal section. The septa reach virtually to the axis. The web-like dissepiments can be seen in cross-section around the margins of the corallite. The longitudinal section shows the tabulae. This genus is common in shallow-water Carboniferous limestones in North America, Europe and Asia. It is often found in association with other corals, including *Lithostrotion*, Brachiopods such as *Productus* and orthocone nautiloids. It grew to about 40mm (1⁵/₈in) in diameter.

▽ **Siphonodendron**

This is a rugose genus with closely clustered corallites. This sectioned specimen clearly shows the internal structure. There are well-developed septa, radiating from the axis. Dissepiments have grown around the corallite walls. Each of the corallites is about 6mm (¹/₄in) in diameter. This genus is found in European Carboniferous rocks.

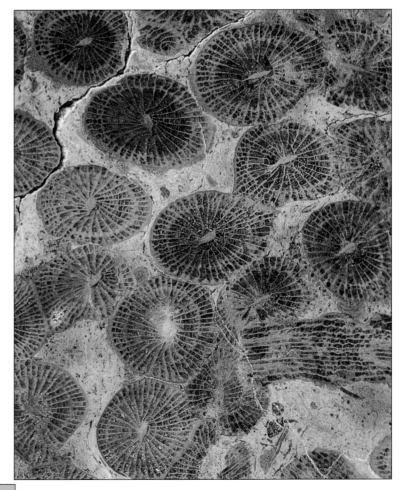

△ **Caninia**

This is a genus of solitary rugose corals. The specimen shown is preserved by replacement of the original calcite by quartz. The septa can be seen radiating from the centre of the corallite and extending vertically down the sides of the coral. There are dissepiments and tabulae, and the margins of the coral show ridges that are characteristic of rugose corals. Although many examples of *Caninia* are tubular, conical forms are also seen. This genus grew in reefs and reef slopes during Carboniferous times, and is associated with molluscs such as *Bellerophon* and *Straparollus*. Brachiopods and other corals were also numerous in this environment. *Caninia* occurs in Carboniferous strata in North America, Europe, Asia, Australia and North Africa. The specimen shown is from Utah, USA.

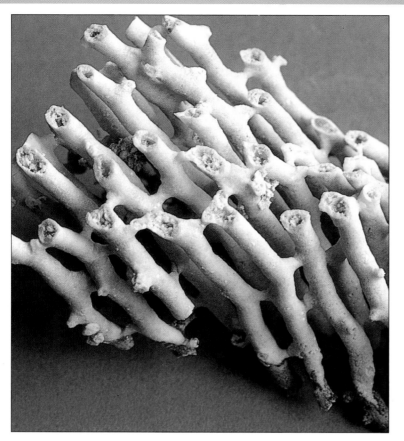

△▽ Lonsdaleia

Two specimens are shown to illustrate the internal detail and the overall structure of this colonial rugose coral. The sectioned specimen shows the radiating septa, which may be separated from the corallite wall by the dissepiments. The complete coral, which is about 100mm (4in) in diameter, shows the moderately deep calices in which the coral polyps lived. This genus is found in rocks from the Carboniferous period in North America, Europe, Asia, North Africa and Australia. It occurred in an environment similar to that of *Dibunophyllum*.

△ Syringopora

This genus is a tabulate coral in which the corallite tubes are divided horizontally by tabulae. The small, pointed septa are visible in the photograph but are absent in some species. Small tubular structures, called tubuli, join the individual corallites. This specimen is 80mm (3¹/₈in) across. *Syringopora* formed large colonies. It is found in Devonian rocks, and in shallow-water limestones from the Carboniferous period.

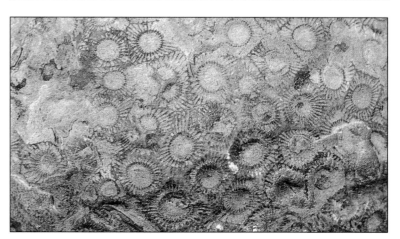

△▷ Acervularia

This colonial rugose coral is shown as a whole specimen and in close-up. The genus is characterized by its thick corallite rims produced by the fusing of dissepiments and septa. It has radiating septa, and the surfaces of the tabulae have a slight upward curve. *Acervularia* lived in shallow-water during the Middle and Upper parts of the Silurian period. It is found fossilized in limestones and shales, often associated with brachiopods and trilobites. This specimen, of which two views are shown, is from Shropshire, UK, is about 60mm (2³/₈in) in diameter.

FOSSIL CLOCKS

Astronomers have calculated that the annual movement of the Earth around the Sun, which causes the seasons, has changed considerably through geological time. It has been worked out that in the Cambrian period, some 550 million years ago, the year was about 424 days long. This means that the Cambrian day was about 20 hours long.

Much evidence from fossils is now available to support the astronomical evidence for the decrease in the number of days per year through time. Corals and their fossils have been used extensively in this work. It is known that modern corals have about 360 growth increments each year. These would seem to be daily additions to the coral structure. This idea is supported by the fact that the algae that live symbiotically with these corals influence coral growth. These algae use photosynthesis only during daylight, and so it seems likely that the corals probably have a similar daily cycle.

Fossil corals, like their present-day equivalents, have fine growth-ridges. Because seasonal patterns are superimposed on the daily pattern, careful study of the growth ridges can determine the annual total.

This table shows how certain coral genera provide evidence about the number of days in a year in prehistoric times that agrees with geophysical calculations.

Coral	Stratigraphic age	Days per year	
		Geophysical estimate	Coral evidence
Streptelasma	Ordovician	408	412
Ketophyllum	Silurian	400	400
Heliophyllum	Devonian	395	385-405
Lithostrotion	Carboniferous	390-396	398
Lophophyllidium	Carboniferous	390-396	380

▽ **Ketophyllum**

This is a solitary rugose coral with a deep calice. The whole corallite is cone-shaped and there may be small 'roots' that help to anchor the structure to the sea floor. These are only rarely preserved. The two sections in the photograph are from the same specimen, which has been divided to reveal the internal and external structure. The outside of the corallite has typical rugose coral ridges. The internal detail consists of tabulae, discontinuous septa and dissepiments. Near to the corallite wall, the tabulae are replaced by dissepiments. This genus occurs in Silurian strata, especially limestones, in Europe and China. This specimen, from Shropshire, UK, is 80mm (3¹/₈in) long.

◁ **Lithostrotion**

This common rugose coral has septa of two types. The major ones are the longer and may join the central axis. The horizontal tabulae curve upwards. *Lithostrotion* flourished in very large colonies. Its fossilized remains are abundant in limestones and it is found in Carboniferous strata in North America, Europe, Asia, North Africa and Australia.

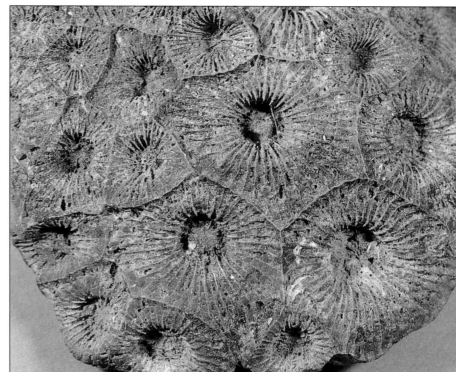

△ **Thysanophyllum**

This is a colonial, rugose coral that has close contact between the individual corallites. These have an angular outline, being either six- or eight-sided. In this example, the septa can be seen reaching almost to the centre of the structure. The walls are thickened with dissepiments. This genus is found in Carboniferous limestones in Europe, and is often associated with other corals and brachiopods. This specimen is 100mm (4in) in diameter.

▷ **Cyathophyllum**

The two specimens shown give some indication of the variation within this rugose genus. The septa are numerous and some extend almost to the centre of the corallite. They take on a spongy appearance around the corallite margin. The calice has only a slight depression. This coral is found in limestones and calcareous shales of the Lower and Middle Devonian period, in North America, Europe, Asia and Australia. The longer specimen is 70mm (2³/₄in) long.

▷ **Thecosmilia**

This is one of the scleractinian corals. It has certain features similar to those of the rugose group, but in the scleractinians the septa are in groups of six, hence the alternative name, hexacorals. The corallites of *Thecosmilia* may branch, and they are often grouped in small colonies. In the photographs the septa can be seen radiating as vertical calcite sheets from the centre of the corallite. Dissepiments strengthen the corallite wall. This genus, along with others that lived during the Mesozoic era, was a reef-builder and existed in warm, shallow seas. Such corals are often fossilized in oolitic limestones. In the sectioned specimen the concentric structure of the ooliths in this rock can be seen. *Thecosmilia* is found in strata ranging from Triassic to Cretaceous in age, worldwide.

JURASSIC REEF ENVIRONMENTS

The patch reef, which was common at times during the Jurassic period, was created by many branching corals, such as *Thecosmilia*, and massive corals, like *Isastrea* and *Thamnastrea*. The sediment deposited on the reef and held together between the corals was rich in calcite and often oolitic and without stratification. The scleractinian corals show many similarities to modern reef-building corals and it is probable that Jurassic forms required similar conditions including warm sea water (over 20°C). Because the algae with which they have a symbiotic relationship need light for photosynthesis, these corals also require shallow water. Patch reefs formed principally in seas with a high salinity where there was significant water movement. The patch reef was home to other forms of life, including bivalve molluscs, brachiopods, sponges, gastropods, starfish and other echinoderms.

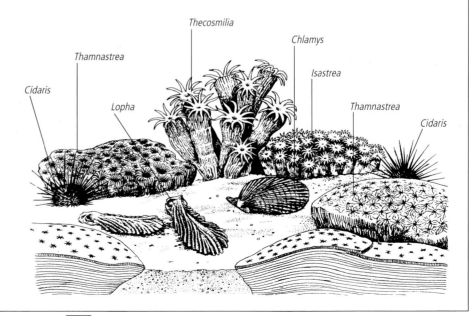

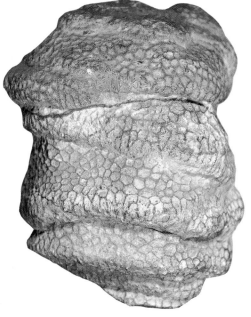

△ Isastraea
This is a colonial scleractinian coral with closely joined six-sided corallites. The entire coral mass forms an irregular tube-shaped structure, with a base narrower than its top surface. The septa are in groups of six and reach from the centre to the margins of each corallite. The corallite walls are strengthened with dissepiments. This is a reef-building coral that is often associated with *Thecosmilia* and *Thamnastrea*. *Isastraea* is found in Jurassic and Cretaceous rocks in North America, Europe and Africa. The whole specimen, of which a detail is shown in close-up, is 100mm (4in) long and comes from southern England.

▷ Thamnastrea
In this sectioned specimen, the corallites and their septa are fused. The corallite walls are virtually absent and the axial structure is very thin. *Thamnastrea* lived during the Mesozoic era and formed large reefs along with other corals such as *Isastraea*. The reefs could reach a diameter of 1.5m (4ft). Like other scleractinian corals, this genus shares many of the features and probably the ecological requirements of modern reef-building corals. Fossils are found in shallow-water limestones and associated strata in North America, South America, Europe and Asia. This specimen was found in Jurassic strata in North Yorkshire, UK.

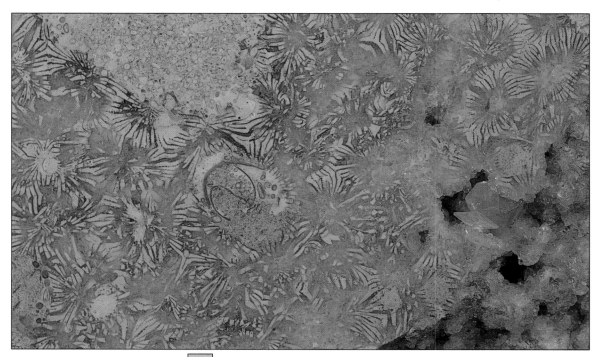

SPONGES

Sponges belong to the phylum known as Porifera. In evolutionary terms, they are thought to come between the early Protozoans (very simple one-celled organisms including Foraminifera and Radiolaria) and the Metazoans (a later group that includes jellyfish and sea-anemones). Sponges are almost exclusively marine organisms and are still commonly found today. Their fossilized remains occur in rocks as old as the Cambrian period.

THE STRUCTURE OF SPONGES

A sponge typically consists of a bag-like structure with an opening on the upper surface and frequently a long stalk beneath. The outer surfaces of this bag are covered in pores that lead into an internal network of water-carrying canals. The central part of the body cavity draws in water by the movement of flagellate collar cells. Food and oxygen are absorbed from the water. Often all that remains of a sponge to become fossilized is the spicules. These durable, siliceous or calcareous spiky structures make up the sponge skeleton and are situated between the two layers of tissue that form the outer wall of the sponge. These spicules are easily fossilized, especially when they are rich in silica. They are believed to be the source of silica from which nodules of chert may be formed. Some cherts contain individual sponge spicules.

▷ **Raphidonema**
A common genus which has an almost flower-like structure, with a narrow base and broad folded upper parts. The thick-walled structure is porous and the tough outer surface is covered with nodules. The skeleton is rigid and is made of spicules with three arms. This calcareous sponge lived from the Triassic to the Cretaceous periods in Europe. It inhabited shallow marine water with its narrow end anchored to the sea bed, and grew to about 50mm (2in) in height. The specimen is from rocks of Cretaceous age in southern England.

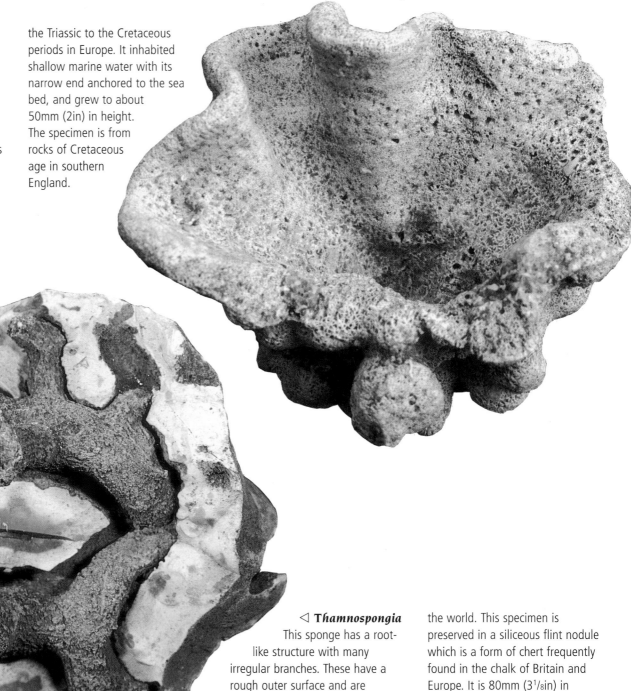

◁ **Thamnospongia**
This sponge has a root-like structure with many irregular branches. These have a rough outer surface and are covered with pores. *Thamnospongia* occurs in Cretaceous rocks all over the world. This specimen is preserved in a siliceous flint nodule which is a form of chert frequently found in the chalk of Britain and Europe. It is 80mm (3^1/8in) in diameter.

S P O N G E   S T R U C T U R E

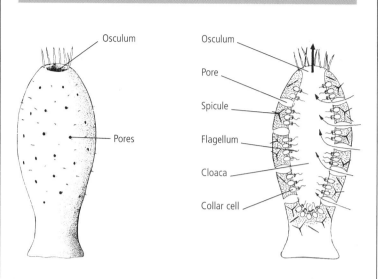

The walls of the sponge are supported by small spikes, or spicules. There are numerous pores, with collar cells lining their openings. The flagella move water currents into the central cavity, the cloaca, and out of the opening at the top, the osculum. The arrows show the direction of the water movement.

△ *Laosciadia (Seliscothon)*

The name *Seliscothon* has been used for this genus, and specimens may be found in collections under either name. It is a rhizomorine sponge, which means it has a root-like structure. The spicules are made of silica, and the overall sponge body has a mushroom-like form with a narrow base. The surfaces are porous. *Laosciadia* is found in Cretaceous rocks in Europe. This specimen is 40mm (1⅝in) in diameter.

▷ *Ventriculites*

This sponge has a skeleton of siliceous spicules that have six branches and join to give a rigid structure. It has a narrow vase-like body and is anchored to the sea bed by a system of 'roots'. *Ventriculites* is covered with many vertical and horizontal grooves. This genus belongs to a group called the Hyalospongea, characterized by thin walls and branching siliceous spicules. Modern relatives of this genus are confined to European waters. Fossil remains of *Ventriculites* are found in Cretaceous rocks in Europe. The specimen shown is about 30mm (1⅛in) long.

◁ *Siphonia*

This genus has siliceous spicules. The overall shape is rather like a tulip flower. It is attached to the sea floor by small roots at the base of the slender stem. The sponge wall is thick and porous. Some branches of the internal canal system cross the sponge radially. Other larger ones run parallel to the outer wall.

These larger canals are for removing water from the sponge while the smaller radial canals bring water into the structure via the pores. *Siphonia* is found in rocks from the Cretaceous and Tertiary periods in Europe. At 30mm (1⅛in) long, the size of this specimen is typical of the genus.

4 ECHINODERMS

This phylum contains a variety of marine creatures characterized by spiny exoskeletons and a five-fold symmetry. Within this classification are the echinoids (sea urchins), asteroids (starfish), crinoids (sea lilies) and ophiuroids (brittle stars). All these classes are well represented in the fossil record, and they are found in rocks dating as far back as the Cambrian period.

CRINOIDS

Echinoderms of this group have an almost plant-like structure, consisting of roots, a stem and a flower-like calyx with delicate arms. The body is held in the calyx, a structure made of large calcite plates, which is held above the sea bed by a slender, fragile stem made of calcite plates called ossicles. These may be rounded in section, star-shaped or hexagonal and their structure and detailed markings vary considerably between species. Crinoidal limestone is largely composed of fragmented stems and broken ossicles. The base of the stem was usually

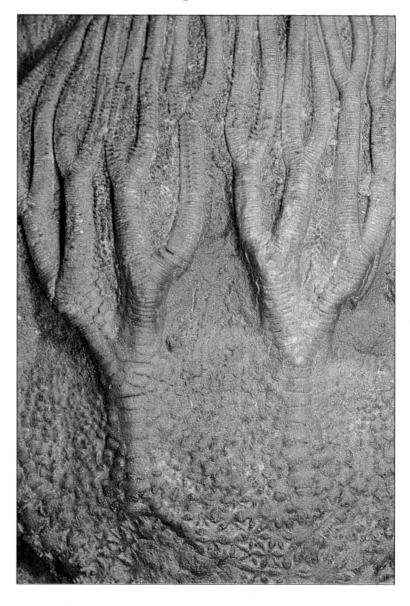

▷ **Scyphocrinites**
This specimen shows part of the calyx and branched arms of a crinoid that grew to a height of over one metre (39in). The segment shown here is 100mm (4in) long. *Scyphocrinites* is characterized by a calyx that is composed of a variety of plates. At the base of the calyx a few large plates are joined to the stem. The upper part of the pear-shaped calyx is composed of numerous smaller plates with the branches growing from among them. At the base of the stem *Scyphocrinites* has a bulbous structure that some suggest served as a float. If this is the case, this crinoid could have been carried significant distances along the sea bed by water currents. The genus has a large geographical range, which supports this theory. Many *Scyphocrinites* fossils have been found with the coprophagus gastropod *Platyceras* on the upper surface of their calyx. These gastropods fed on the *Scyphocrinites'* waste products. This crinoid is found in Upper Silurian and Devonian strata. In some areas its broken remains, especially ossicles, have accumulated to form masses of 'scyphocrinite limestone'. *Scyphocrinites* occurs in North America, (especially the Lower Devonian strata of southeastern Missouri and Oklahoma), Europe, Africa and Asia. The specimen illustrated here is from Devonian strata at Alnif, North Africa.

CRINOID STRUCTURE

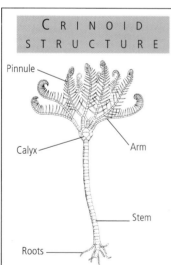

Pinnule

Calyx

Arm

Stem

Roots

The stem is secured to the sea bed by short roots. At the top of the stem lies the calyx, which holds the soft body of the organism. The arms, with their feathery pinnules, wave in the water and act as a funnel for food particles.

◁ **Echinoderm-rich chalk**
Cretaceous chalk cliffs are often rich in fossil echinoderms.

held to the sea bed or to algae by root-like structures, but some crinoids moved freely along the sea bed. The arms often branch to form a net-like structure that funnelled food towards the central mouth. A food groove covered in cilia (tiny hairs) can be seen on each arm. The movement of the cilia swept the food into the mouth.

From the evidence of fossils and by analogy with modern forms, we can be reasonably sure that crinoids lived colonially. Today modern crinoids live in both cold and tropical seas, and at a variety of depths.

▽ *Crinoid ossicles*
The stems of crinoids are composed of rounded ossicles, which often break off from the fossils. This specimen of impure Carboniferous limestone contains many different ossicles that became fragmented from the stem before fossilization.

▷ *Macrocrinus*

This photograph shows the fossilized calices of two crinoids. One retains a reasonable length of stem. This genus has between 12 and 16 stout arms. The calyx is small. Here the pinnules give the arms a feathery appearance and form an open funnel to the crinoid's mouth, deep in the centre of the calyx. The pinnules with their minute filaments (called cirri) create a food-gathering net. This genus is found in Lower Carboniferous strata in North America. Many fine specimens have come from Indiana. The larger of the two specimens shown is about 40mm (1⁵/₈in) long.

LIME MUD COMMUNITY

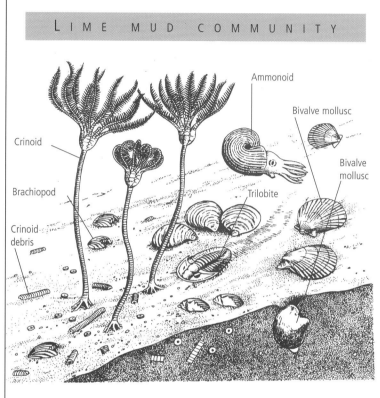

Ammonoid
Bivalve mollusc
Crinoid
Bivalve mollusc
Brachiopod
Trilobite
Crinoid debris

These organisms make up a typical sea-bed community at the foot of an early Carboniferous reef slope.

◁ *Clematocrinus*

The calyx of this small crinoid is shown. The arms have many slender branches and here they are folded towards each other. The branches have numerous smaller pinnules growing from them. As is common with most fossil crinoids, the stem, of which only a small part is present here, is fragmented between the individual ossicles. *Clematocrinus* is found in Middle Silurian rocks in North America, Europe and Australia. This specimen is 25mm (1in) long.

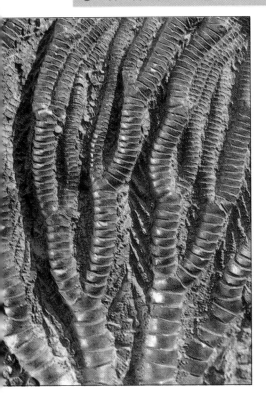

▷ Woodocrinus

The arms of this genus characteristically branch into two or four above the calyx which is composed of large plates. The rounded stem tapers to a point and lacks any roots. This specimen shows the calyx and arms. *Woodocrinus* is restricted to Carboniferous strata in Europe. Good examples have been found in the Carboniferous rocks of northern England, from where this specimen comes. It is 40mm (1⅝in) across.

△ Pentacrinites

A characteristic feature of this genus is the star-shape of the ossicles, which are often found as separate fossils. The calyx is quite small but the arms are long and the stem can be over one metre (39in) long. It has many arms, which are subdivided and densely packed with pinnules. Modern forms of this genus are not attached to the sea bed, whereas *Pentacrinites* was rooted to the sea bed in great masses. It has also been found fossilized, attached to driftwood. Fossils of this genus are frequently preserved in pyrite, as in the example shown. It occurs in rocks ranging in age from Triassic to Pliocene in North America (including good examples from the Jurassic strata of California), and Europe, where it is also especially common in Jurassic rocks.

▽ Encrinus

This crinoid has a small calyx but well-developed arms. The plates that form the calyx can be clearly seen in this specimen. The lowest of the plates are the basals, followed by the brachials. The radials are uppermost. This arrangement gives *Encrinus* perfect pentameral (fivefold) symmetry. The genus has ten arms with numerous pinnules. It is common in European Middle and Upper Triassic strata, especially in Germany in the Muschelkalk formation, where whole specimens are often preserved intact. The remains of this and other crinoids are so abundant that crinoidal limestones make up a great percentage of the strata. By analogy with modern relatives and by a careful study of its structure and the rocks in which it is found, it has been suggested that *Encrinus* lived in shallow, flowing sea water with its calyx facing the current. The densely packed pinnules caught microscopic food particles, such as algae and crustacean larvae, from the moving water. This specimen is from the Muschelkalk and is 35mm (1⅜in) in length.

ASTEROIDS AND OPHIUROIDS

These two classes include starfish and similar creatures. Within the ophiuroid genus are the brittle stars, which can be recognized by their very slender arms. The asteroids have stouter arms and a more obviously star-like appearance. Unlike those of the ophiuroids, the arms of asteroids are not clearly separated from the central disc. Both groups are found as fossils, although not as commonly as other echinoderms. However, great masses of starfish have been found fossilized together forming 'starfish beds'.

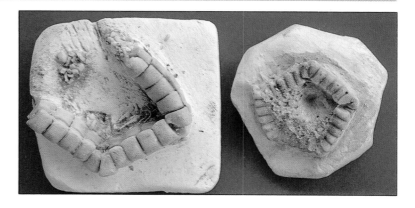

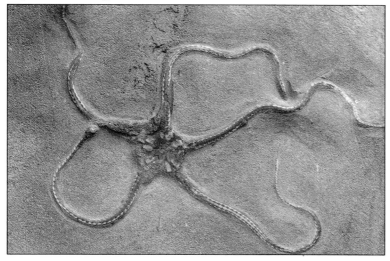

△ Palaeocoma

This brittle star is found principally in Jurassic strata in Europe. They often occur in groups. The slender arms, which radiate from the small central disc, have small spines. The mouth is positioned centrally on the undersurface. *Palaeocoma* is a close relative of modern brittle stars and has been found in rocks ranging in age from Jurassic to Cretaceous.

△ Metopaster

This asteroid genus had no arms. There is a pentagonal perimeter made of large plates and an internal mass of much smaller plates. On the undersurface there is a distinctive arrangement of plates. However, on the upper surface the very small plates are arranged in a seemingly unorganized fashion.

Often fossils of this genus consist only of isolated plates, but sometimes material such as that shown here is found. *Metopaster* occurs in strata of Upper Cretaceous to Miocene age in North America, Europe and New Zealand. It grows up to 60mm (2³/₈in) in diameter.

△ Orepanaster

This ophiuroid is from a starfish bed near Girvan in southern Scotland. It measures about 50mm (2in) across. Its body consists of a central stellate disc surrounded by a larger round structure. The slender arms extend from the inner disc and radiate outwards. The arms are thin and fragile. The Girvan starfish bed is of Upper Ordovician age and is a greyish-green calcareous sandstone. As well as the characteristic starfishes, it also contains other echinoderms, corals, trilobites, brachiopods and gastropods.

△ Lapworthura

This is an ancient ophiuroid with five slender arms radiating from the small central disc. The arms, which have serrated, spinose margins, are composed of ossicles and are easily fragmented. *Lapworthura* is found in Ordovician and Silurian strata in Europe and Australia. The specimen shown here, which is about 50mm (2in) across is from northern England. Many fine specimens have also been found in Middle Silurian strata in Herefordshire, England.

ECHINOIDS

This class contains the sea urchins, which are well known for their spiny shells. This shell, or test, can be rounded, heart-shaped, domed or flattened. These marine-dwelling creatures have a long history. The earliest echinoids have been found fossilized in Ordovician strata, and their descendants are common around the world today.

ECHINOID STRUCTURE

The test is made of interlocking calcareous plates and is covered with a thin, skin-like membrane. The plates can be divided into two groups, both of which are in five bands running completely or, in some genera, only partially around the test. The smaller, ambulacral plates are in narrow bands. These plates have tube feet, which are small, tentacle-like structures joined to the creature's internal vascular system. They are used for respiration and movement. The creature can extend a tube foot by filling it with water. The rounded disc on its far end acts as a sucker. The wider bands of plates are the interambulacra.

The peristome (the group of plates around the mouth), which contains the mouth, is on the lower, or oral, surface of the test. The periproct, the structure that contains the anus, is on the upper, or aboral, surface in many genera. In some echinoids, however, the anus has migrated during evolution to the side or to the oral surface of the test. The outer surface of the test is usually covered with spines. These vary between species from thin needles to stout club-shaped stuctures. The interior of the test contains the fluid-filled body.

Two groups of echinoids are recognized, the regular and irregular echinoids. The former have pentameral (five-fold) symmetry and the mouth and anus are centrally placed. In the irregular group the symmetry is bilateral. The ambulacral plates do not necessarily encircle the test, and the mouth and anus are not always central.

◁ *Paracidaris*
A single spine of this genus is shown preserved in pale limestone of Upper Jurassic age from France. The longitudinal ribs with closely spaced nodules are typical of many echinoid genera.

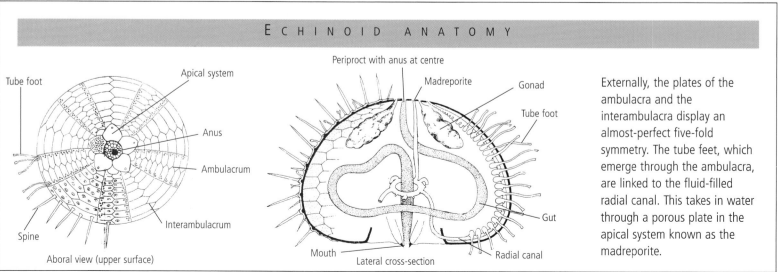

ECHINOID ANATOMY

Tube foot · Apical system · Anus · Ambulacrum · Interambulacrum · Spine · Aboral view (upper surface)

Periproct with anus at centre · Madreporite · Gonad · Tube foot · Gut · Mouth · Radial canal · Lateral cross-section

Externally, the plates of the ambulacra and the interambulacra display an almost-perfect five-fold symmetry. The tube feet, which emerge through the ambulacra, are linked to the fluid-filled radial canal. This takes in water through a porous plate in the apical system known as the madreporite.

◁ *Plegiocidaris*

This regular echinoid has a test covered with numerous large bosses to which stout spines were attached with a ball and socket joint. The mouth is placed centrally on the underside of the test, and the anus centrally on the top. In this illustration the test is viewed from the side to show the ambulacra and the boss-bearing interambulacra. The spines of this genus are very like those of *Paracidaris* (see page 57). *Plegiocidaris* is found in strata from the Upper Triassic to the Jurassic periods in Europe. The test of this species grows to about 30mm (1¹/₈in) in diameter.

▷ *Cidaris*

This specimen has been preserved with many of its long thick spines attached. This is fairly unusual because the spines are easily broken off; in this example the test itself has been crushed. *Cidaris* is a regular echinoid with a rounded test and pentameral symmetry. It has a central mouth and anus. The spines, which may be thin, or stout and club-shaped, are attached to the test by robust bosses (tubercles). This genus is found in strata ranging in age from Jurassic to Recent.

◁ *Clypeus*

This relatively large irregular echinoid is characterized by its flattened test, which has a deep groove on the aboral surface. The anus is positioned in this groove. The ambulacra are petaloid on the dorsal surface and have slit-like pores. The symmetry of the test is bilateral because of the variation in the ambulacra and the position of the anus. This is a common genus in Jurassic strata in Europe, Africa and Australia. A typical specimen is 70mm (2³/₄in) in diameter.

◁ **Pygaster**

This irregular echinoid differs only slightly from the regular forms, in that its anus is placed only just off-centre. The periproct forms a key-hole shape close to the apex. The ambulacra are thin and relatively straight, and the attachment points for the thin spines are small. The overall shape of the test is pentagonal rather than rounded.

Pygaster is common in shallow marine strata of Jurassic and Cretaceous age in Europe. It burrowed into mud and oolitic sand in an environment similar to that found around the Bahamas today. Fossils associated with *Pygaster* include gastropods and bivalves. The specimen shown is 60mm (2³/₈in) in diameter.

◁▽ **Micraster**

This well-known irregular echinoid has a heart-shaped test. The oral and aboral surfaces can be seen in one photograph [below] and the aboral surface of another specimen (left) preserved in brown flint. In this genus the anus is placed high on the posterior end of the test, with a slight ridge above it. The ambulacra are petaloid and atrophied, and the test is covered with small bosses for spines. There are a number of different species of *Micraster*, and its evolutionary sequence is well-documented. Over time this genus developed a broader, higher test; the petaloid ambulacra became elongated; the surface of the test became increasingly granular; the anterior groove, which extended to the mouth, deepened; and the mouth itself moved forwards, and developed a projecting labrum (lip). The labrum can be seen on the oral surface of the palest specimen shown (below left).

Micraster burrowed into the soft mud of the sea bed. It was especially common in the chalk sea of the Cretaceous period. It is, however, found in strata from the Cretaceous to Palaeocene periods in Europe. Particularly fine specimens come from the chalk strata of southern England, including the collections used for evolutionary and stratigraphic study. Species of *Micraster* are used as zone fossils, for subdivisions of the Upper Cretaceous period. The specimens shown are of typical size at about 50mm (2in) in diameter.

▷ Holaster

Although this genus is thought to be related to *Echinocorys* (page 60), it differs from that genus in having a slightly heart-shaped test, the posterior end being rather pointed. The anus is on this part of the test. The aboral surface is slightly domed and the oral surface is flat. The pores are paired and slit-like. The ambulacra are petaloid and are separated by wide interambulacral areas. The anterior ambulacrum is situated in a groove which leads to the mouth. This genus is found in Cretaceous to Eocene strata, and has a worldwide distribution. It is common in the Cretaceous sandstone. *Holaster* is used as a zone fossil for part of the Upper Cretaceous period. It is found fossilized with molluscs such as *Chlamys*, *Inoceramus*, *Spondylus*, *Mantelliceras*, and *Turrilites*. The specimen shown is 90mm (3¹/₂in) in diameter.

◁ Holectypus

This is an irregular echinoid with a centrally placed mouth. The anus is on the oral surface in some species and on the margin of this surface in others. The overall shape is slightly domed, with a flattened oral surface. The ambulacra are reasonably straight and extend around the test from the centre of the aboral surface to the mouth. *Holectypus* is found in North America and Europe in Jurassic and Cretaceous strata. The specimen illustrated is 20mm (³/₄in) in diameter.

▷ Hemipneustes

These irregular echinoids grew to large size and may be 100mm (4in) in diameter. The specimen shown is 60mm (2³/₈in) in diameter. The test is rounded or ovoid and, viewed from the side has a high dome-shape. The symmetry is bilateral; the anus is at the back of the test and the mouth is at the front. The ambulacrum at the front of the test is in a slight groove. The surface of the test is smooth and the pores in the ambulacral plates are paired and elongated. *Hemipneustes* is found in Cretaceous strata in Europe, and related modern genera are found in the Far East and in the Indian Ocean. They live at depths of 250-900m (800-3,000ft).

▽ **Cassidulus**

This small, irregular echinoid has atrophied petaloid ambulacra, only just visible on this example. They form a star-shape on the aboral surface. *Cassidulus* and its relatives can be distinguished from other echinoids by a flower-like structure, called a floscelle, around the peristome. The floscelle consists of bulges in the interambulacral plates and flattened ambulacral plates. The test has a flattened overall shape with the highest part of the aboral surface to the front. *Cassidulus* is found in strata of Eocene to Recent age in North America, and is typically about 40mm (1⁵/₈in) in diameter.

△ **Echinocorys**

This irregular genus has a high-domed test with a flat base. The anus is on the aboral surface near the posterior margin. The ambulacra are quite straight. This genus is found in Cretaceous strata in North America, Europe, Asia Minor, Madagascar, Cuba and the CIS. The specimen shown is 80mm (3¹/₈in) in diameter. *Echinocorys* is found fossilized with many creatures that lived in the chalk seas of Europe. These include the echinoid *Micraster*, molluscs such as *Inoceramus*, and the sponges *Ventriculites* and *Seliscothon*. *Echinocorys* is thought to have lived partially buried in the soft sediment of the sea bed.

◁ **Dendraster**

Generally referred to as sand dollars, this irregular genus has an oval test which is very flattened and typical of the group. The petaloid ambulacra are atrophied and the apical system, which is at their centre, is in a posterior position on the aboral surface of the test. The pores in the ambulacra are slit-like. There is a groove above the anus which is on the oral surface at the edge of the test. *Dendraster* is common in Pliocene and younger strata in North America, especially California, where tests of *Dendraster* are so frequent that they form a substantial part of the rock. It grows to about 60mm (2³/₈in) in diameter.

◁ **Lovenia**
An irregular genus that is characterized by a heart-shaped test, which has a marked groove at the back. The ambulacra are wide and almost triangular. They have wide notches on their margins. The front ambulacrum has, in effect, been replaced by the groove. The surface of the test is rough and a number of large recessed tubercles can be seen in the interambulacral areas. *Lovenia* is well known from Australia in strata from Eocene to Recent in age. It grows to about 40mm ($1^5/_8$in) in diameter.

▽**Amphiope**
This is a rather strangely shaped, flattened echinoid. The overall outline of the test is rounded, but there are two distinct notches at the back. The oral surface (below) has a covering of small pores. Y-shaped grooves radiate from the mouth. The aboral surface (below left) has stunted petaloid ambulacra, which form a 'feathery' star shape. The anus is situated on the back edge of the oral surface. *Amphiope* is found in Oligocene to Miocene strata in Europe and India. It grew to about 30mm ($1^1/_8$in) in diameter.

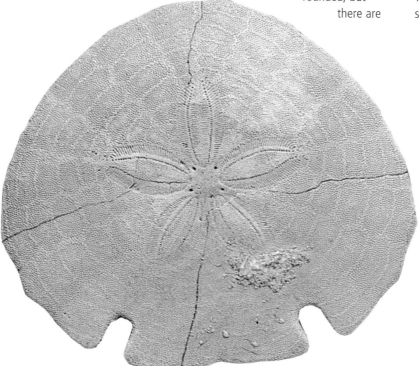

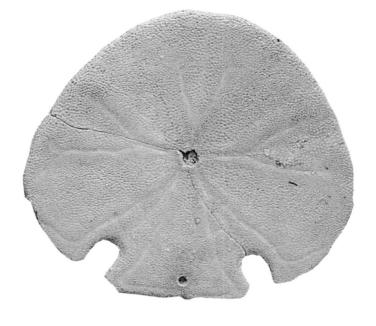

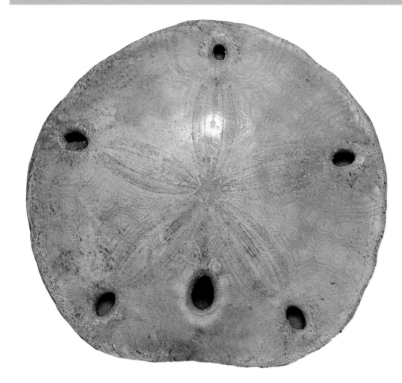

▽ Echinoid Way of Life

Echinoids are exclusively marine organisms. The different species live at depths, varying from very shallow intertidal waters to abyssal ocean deeps. Echinoids that have rounded often very spiny tests, can wedge themselves into rock cavities and hollows. Other echinoids use their spines and tube feet for movement, climbing over rocky sea beds. In shallow waters some regular genera, such as *Cidaris*, use their massive spines to hold them into rock cavities, while others use large sucker-like tube feet to withstand the action of currents and waves. The irregular forms are adapted to living in a great variety of situations. The heart-shaped echinoids are adept at burrowing into the sea-floor sediment. Those that burrowed deeply, including species of *Micraster*, developed a wide sub-anal fasciole. This is a band of small spines equipped with cilia which can move water currents across the test. The fasciole helps to keep the burrow reasonably clean by encouraging a flow of water away from the test into the offshoot of the burrow constructed for waste.

Another very numerous group are the flattened or domed echinoids known as 'sand dollars'. *Clypeaster* is a common example. These sea urchins have tests that may be slightly submerged in the sediment or may be buried at an angle to the surface with half of the test protruding. Some genera have a test that resembles a miniature sand dune which allows the sediment to move over it efficiently. The regular echinoids live on a variety of food. Some are active carnivores and pursue sponges and worms. The irregular types tend to feed on micro-organisms and debris sifted from the water or the sediment.

△ *Encope*

This irregular genus lived in large masses on, or just below the surface of the sand of the sea bed. It lives today in shallow water about 200m (650 ft) deep. *Encope* is often called the 'keyhole' sea urchin because of the holes in its test and especially the large oval opening, or lunule, in the interambulacrum at the back of the test. The ambulacra are atrophied and petaloid and have slit-like pores along their margins. In this genus, the mouth and anus are close together on the underside (oral surface). Also on the oral surface of the test, there are pairs of shallow, vein-like grooves, called actinal furrows. These lead from the mouth to the test margin, spreading out around the five holes. The actinal furrows bring food towards the mouth. Echinoids such as *Encope* have a covering of fur-like spines. This genus is found in strata of Miocene to Recent age in North America, South America and the West Indies. This specimen is from San Diego, California and is 90mm (3¹/₂in) in diameter.

▽ *Parmulechinus*

This small irregular disc-shaped echinoid has a very flattened test with a slight central dome. It lived near the surface of the soft sea bed sediment. The ambulacra are petaloid and atrophied. They form a star-shape on the aboral surface. The mouth is at the centre of the oral surface. The interambulacra are composed of large plates. This genus is found in Oligocene strata in north Africa and Europe. The specimens shown are typical at about 15mm (⁵/₈in) in diameter.

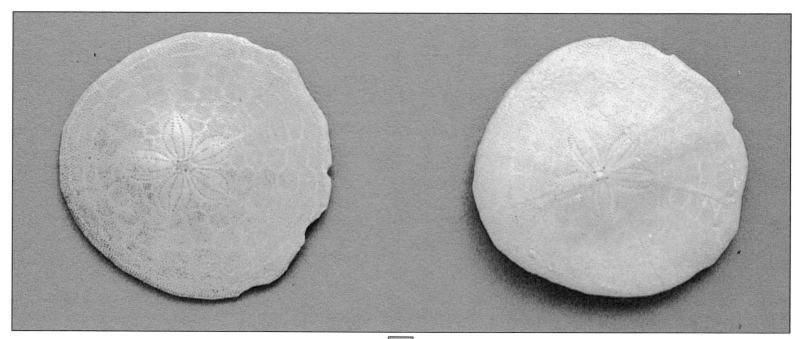

▽▷ *Clypeaster*

These large irregular echinoids have tests with a rounded or sub-pentagonal outline and a dome-shaped profile. The underside is flat. The ambulacra are wide and petaloid and do not reach the test margin. There are slit-like pores on the edges of the ambulacra and a star-shaped plate and five smaller plates at the centre of the upper (aboral) surface. The periproct lies on the oral surface at the posterior margin of the test. The peristome and mouth are at the centre of the oral surface in a deep hollow. There are five straight actinal furrows leading to the mouth. The mouth has strong jaws that enabled *Clypeaster* to feed on animal and vegetable debris that it sifted from the sea-bed sediment. The high-domed test is supported inside by pillars. This genus contains the largest known echinoids and the specimens shown are typical at 120mm (4³/₄in) in diameter. *Clypeaster* lives today in shallow, tropical seas, burrowing slightly into the loose sediment of the sea bed. Cilia in the grooves on the oral side of the test maintain the movement of water towards the mouth. *Clypeaster* lives in great colonies and is often fossilized in groups as shown. Its fossils are found in strata of Upper Eocene to Recent age all over the world.

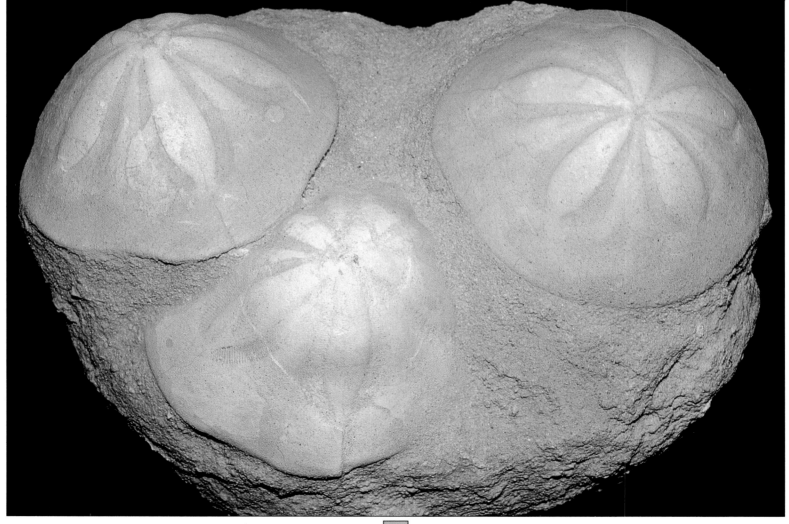

CHAPTER 5 BRACHIOPODS

There have been periods in the past when this phylum of shelled marine organisms had far more representatives than it has today. There are now fewer brachiopods than molluscs. Brachiopods first appear in the fossil record during the Cambrian period, and they, like many other groups of organisms, must have evolved from soft-bodied Pre-Cambrian ancestors. Today they live in a variety of environments including both warm and cool seas, especially in the Far East around New Zealand, Japan and Australia.

BRACHIOPOD ANATOMY

Diductor muscles

Pedicle valve

Lophophore

Brachial valve

Pedicle

Adductor muscles

This cross-section shows the internal structure of a brachiopod based on what we know about modern genera. The upper, pedicle valve is significantly larger than the lower, brachial valve. The pedicle valve has an opening through which a tough stalk, the pedicle, emerges. This secures the creature to the sea bed. In articulate brachiopods the valves are opened and closed by the combined action of two groups of muscles, the adductor and the diductor muscles. The coiled structure in the centre of the shell is the lophophore. The grooves in the lophophore assist the passage of food to the mouth.

◁△ **Reef limestone**
Here a mass of reef limestone contains two brachiopod shells and

a crinoid ossicle surrounded by bryzoans in what was originally lime mud.

THE CHARACTERISTICS OF BRACHIOPODS

From the outside, a brachiopod shell looks rather like that of a bivalve mollusc, such as a mussel. However, apart from the fact that both groups have two valves to their shell, there is little similarity between the two groups. Unlike the bivalve mollusc, the two valves of the brachiopod are different from each other in a number of ways. Moreover, the plane of symmetry passes through the middle of each valve. The valves are thus dorsal and ventral in position. In most bivalve molluscs the symmetry is between the valves. The ventral, or pedicle, valve of the brachiopod is the larger of the two, and it has an opening in the posterior end through which, in life, a fleshy stalk called the pedicle protruded. This anchored the animal to the sea bed, or in the case of burrowers like *Lingula* to the base of the burrow. Some forms were without a functional pedicle and lay on the sea bed. The dorsal, or brachial, valve contains an organ peculiar to the brachiopods. This is the lophophore, a curved ciliated structure on which food (in the sea water drawn into the shell) is trapped. In some fossils, the brachidium – a calcareous support for the lophophore – is preserved.

CLASSES OF BRACHIOPOD

There are two classes within this phylum. The 'inarticulate' brachiopods are the more primitive of the two and are unable to move their valves in relation to each other. In this class the shell may be calcareous, although it is often composed of alternating layers of chitin and calcium phosphate. In contrast, the 'articulate' brachiopods have a shell of fibrous calcite, and are able to move their valves independently by means of a mechanism of muscles and hinges. One set of muscles, the adductors, are used to close the valves; the diductors open the valves. Most brachiopods are about 50mm (2in) in length, although some are as much as 350mm (14in).

△ Lingula

This common inarticulate brachiopod is found all over the world in strata ranging from Ordovician to Recent in age, and must rank as one of the longest living genera. It has an oval outline and the valves display many thin ribs and growth lines. The shell is thin and commonly has muscle scars on the inside surface. The valves are almost equal in size and are convex. *Lingula* is a burrower and today it burrows to a depth of 300mm (12in) into the sea bed. It is fastened in the burrow by a long pedicle, and feeds through the open anterior end of the shell, which is uppermost in the burrow. Because modern species can live in brackish water, its fossils provide important evidence when ancient environ-ments are being reconstructed. In Silurian marine strata *Lingula* is found with a number of other brachiopods, but when the water became brackish, the total number of species was reduced, with *Lingula* often being the only fossil. In Triassic times shallow lagoons existed in Britain, which had formed as the sea flooded previously dry land. *Lingula* occurs in the rocks formed in these lagoons along with bivalve molluscs such as *Pholadomya* and *Modiolus*.

◁ Lingulella

This inarticulate brachiopod has an almost oval shell outline with virtually no external detail. The valves are slightly convex and have fine radiating lines on their internal surfaces. The pedicle valve has a small groove for the pedicle. The slab of rock shown here contains many fossils of this genus. *Lingulella* is found worldwide in strata from the Cambrian to the Ordovician periods. This brachiopod lives in both shallow- and deep-water environments. The rock specimen shown comes from Portmadog, Wales.

▷ Heterorthis

This genus of articulate brachiopods is almost circular in outline with a convex pedicle valve and a flat or slightly concave brachial valve. The outside of the shell is ornamented with ribs which radiate from the umbo (the beak-shaped end of the valves). There are also concentric growth lines. The hinge line is almost straight. In the pictured specimen the internal part of the valves is preserved. This genus occurs in strata of Ordovician age in North America and Europe, especially in sedimentary rocks formed in fairly shallow water. The shell has an average diameter of about 35mm (1³/₈in).

▽ Atrypa

This articulate brachiopod with a biconvex shell has an almost flat pedicle valve. The brachial valve is rounded. The pedicle valve is shown in the photograph. Both valves are ornamented with ribs, concentric growth lines and slight ridges. The margin of the valves is slightly flared. This common genus is found in rocks of Silurian to Devonian age, worldwide, and occurs in shallow marine strata. Juveniles were attached by the pedicle to the sea floor, adults rested on their brachial valves. *Atrypa* is found with a great variety of other fossils including other brachiopods, trilobites, corals, molluscs and crinoids.

△ Orthis

This is an articulate brachiopod which has an almost rounded shell outline and a short hinge margin. The pedicle valve is convex and the brachial valve flat, or very slightly convex. Sharp ribs are seen on the outside of the shell. On this slab of micaceous sandstone from Shropshire, UK, some of the internal features are also visible. This brachiopod and its relatives lived attached to the sea bed, usually in shallow water. It is found worldwide in Ordovician strata.

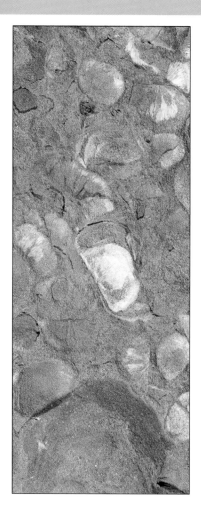

▷ Orbiculoidea

This inarticulate brachiopod has a rounded shell, composed of chitin and phosphates. Each valve is somewhat conical, the brachial valve being the flatter of the two. The valves are ornamented with radiating ribs and thin growth lines. The slit-like pedicle opening lies in a groove that runs from the posterior margin of the shell to the central apex. *Orbiculoidea* grows to about 20mm (³/₄in) in width and is found in a variety of sedimentary rocks of Ordovician to Permian age, worldwide. It lived attached by the pedicle to the sea bed. Because it is found fossilized in deep-water black shales along with graptolites and a meagre variety of other brachiopods, it has been suggested that *Orbiculoidea* also attached itself to floating seaweed.

△ Sowerbyella

This is an articulate brachiopod with a convex pedicle valve and a concave brachial valve. The hinge line is straight and the overall shell outline roughly semi-circular. It lived on the sea bed, lying on its pedicle valve. The genus is found in a variety of rocks including sandstone and mudstone. The specimens pictured here show internal and external details. The outsides of the valves are ornamented with radiating ribs. *Sowerbyella* is found in Ordovician strata with worldwide distribution. It probably lived in waters where there were no strong currents. It grew to about 15mm (⁵/₈in) in diameter.

▽ Spirifer

This well-known articulate brachiopod has a semicircular shell with a long, straight hinge line, which forms the widest part of the shell. Both valves are convex, and in this specimen the beak of the pedicle valve can be seen protruding above the hinge line. There is a fold in the brachial valve and a groove (sulcus) in the pedicle valve. There are prominent radial ribs on the shell surface, as well as growth lines, which may be slightly spinose. *Spirifer* could grow to a width of about 120mm (5in) and is found in Carboniferous strata, worldwide. It is commonly fossilized in limestones, indicating shallow water environments, including reef margins where it occurs with other brachiopods such as *Productus* and *Schizophoria*, crinoids, bivalve molluscs, and orthocone nautiloids.

◁ Leptaena

The shell of this articulate brachiopod is heavily ornamented with ribs and wavy concentric ridges. It has a convex pedicle valve and a flat brachial valve. The straight hinge line has 'ears'. The posterior area of the shell is almost flat and the anterior bends at a steep angle. *Leptaena* grew to a width of about 50mm (2in). *Leptaena* lived all over the world during Ordovician, Silurian and Devonian times. In the Ordovician period it flourished in continental shelf areas with other brachiopods, trilobites, gastropods and nautiloids.

▷ *Schizophoria*

With an almost rectangular shell, this articulate brachiopod has a maximum width that is about half its length. The valves are both convex but the brachial valve is more curved. Each valve is shown, the darker valve on the left is the pedicle valve. The surface of the shell is ornamented with fine ribs. *Schizophoria* is similar in shape to a number of other creatures. This may be a result of a common evolutionary response to the environment. Such similarity in outward form is called homeomorphy and can occur in unrelated genera living at different times. This phenomenon occurs in many phyla. *Schizophoria* grew to a width of about 50mm (2in). It lived during Silurian to Permian times,

with a worldwide distribution. The pictured specimen is from Carboniferous strata in France. The

rocks in which it is found indicate that it lived with other brachiopods, bivalve molluscs and crinoids.

▽ *Productus*

This articulate brachiopod belongs to a group called productids. Some productids grew to a great size – *Gigantoproductus* can reach a width of over 150mm (6in). *Productus*, however, is usually about 40mm (1⅝in) in width. This genus has a convex pedicle valve (shown in the photograph) and a concave or flat brachial valve. It is roughly semicircular in outline, but the hinge line is straight. The outer surfaces of the valves are ornamented with ribs and growth

lines. Though not often preserved in fossils, the shell had spines, which held it to the sea floor. *Productus* is found in strata of Carboniferous age in Europe and Asia. The productids have a worldwide distribution in rocks ranging from Upper Ordovician to Permian age. *Productus* fossils have been found in limestones characteristic of reef-slopes. Other creatures in such strata include other brachiopods, bivalve molluscs and crinoids. *Productus* is also found in muddy strata representing deeper environments.

△ *Pustula*

This articulate brachiopod has an almost rectangular outline with a straight hinge line. The umbo (the beak-shaped end of the valves) is small and pointed with numerous concentric growth lines. Faint ribs cross the shell from the umbo to the margin. The pedicle valve, seen here, is convex and the brachial valve is flat. This is a relatively large brachiopod that grew to about 120mm (5in) in width. It is found in Europe in Carboniferous rocks. The specimen shown is from Staffordshire, UK. *Pustula* fossils are found in limestones and other shallow-water sediments along with other brachiopods, molluscs and corals.

△ **Unispirifer**

This articulate brachiopod, belonging to the spiriferid group, has a wide, straight hinge line that forms the widest part of the shell. The overall shape is semicircular. Both valves are convex and are ornamented with ribs, which radiate from the umbo. There are also faint growth lines. Some of the ribs branch in two. In the photograph, the larger pedicle valve can be seen behind the brachial valve. As with other spiriferids, *Unispirifer* has a spiral structure inside the brachial valve that supported the lophophore. It is found in Carboniferous rocks, with a worldwide distribution, and grew to a width of about 120mm (5in).

▷ **Stiphrothyris**

This articulate brachiopod has an elongated, ovoid shell. The pedicle valve is larger than the brachial valve and has a large pedicle opening. In the anterior part of the shell there is a deep fold, or sulcus. There are faint growth lines visible on the shell. In this specimen, the brachial valve has been broken open to reveal the internal calcareous loop, the brachidium. *Stiphrothyris* was attached to the sea bed by its fleshy pedicle and is found in shallow-water Jurassic strata in Europe. It grew to about 40mm (1⅝in) in length.

◁ **Tetrarhynchia**

Tetrarhynchia is often found in Jurassic strata in North America and Europe. This articulate brachiopod has a sub-triangular shell, ornamented with stout ribs. The umbo is small, pointed and curved. The pedicle opening is small. Both valves are convex and the margin of the shell has a folded appearance. *Tetrarhynchia* grew to a maximum width of about 140mm (5½in), but most examples are much smaller. It is often found fossilized in groups. It is preserved in Jurassic sandstones with molluscs, ammonites and belemnites. Another characteristic Jurassic environment in which *Tetrarhynchia* is found is the hardground. This occurs where the sea bed of the time was a hard rock surface. On such surfaces various boring and burrowing organisms thrived, along with creatures that rested on the sea bed. Here *Tetrarhynchia* is found with ammonites, such as *Amaltheus*, bivalve molluscs, including *Pseudopecten*, corals, crinoids and echinoids.

▽ **Stenoscisma**

This articulate brachiopod has a prominent umbo and an overall ovoid shape. The valves are both convex and strongly ribbed. These specimens are internal casts, the shell having been removed, probably by waters circulating through the sediment in which the shells were buried. It is small, reaching only about 20mm (¾in) in diameter. It is found in strata from the Devonian to Permian periods, with a worldwide distribution. The pictured specimens are from Permian reef limestones of Durham, UK. *Stenoscisma* was apparently able to withstand the highly saline waters of the shallow reef-top environment.

▷ **Goniorhynchia**

The shell of this articulate brachiopod has an almost triangular outline and convex valves. The brachial valve is slightly smaller than the pedicle valve. The umbo is pointed, with a small pedicle opening. The shell surface is ornamented with strong radiating ribs, and the margin is folded. *Goniorhynchia* lived attached to the sea bed and is often found in Jurassic sandstone strata. This genus occurs in Jurassic strata in Europe and grew to a width of about 30mm (1⅛in).

▽ **Isjuminella**

This distinctive articulate brachiopod has an unusual shell. The convex valves are curved and the overall appearance is globose. The shell surface is ornamented with strong ribs and zig-zag lines that follow the pattern of the valve margins. This brachiopod lived on shallow-water sea beds and is found in strata of Jurassic age in Russia and Europe. It grew to about 100mm (4in) in width.

◁ Terebratella

Terebratella is an articulate brachiopod with an ovoid shell. The pedicle valve extends beyond the brachial valve near the beak. Both the valves are convex and the pedicle opening is visible just below the beak. The external surfaces of the valves are ornamented with numerous delicate ribs radiating from the beak, some of which divide in two (bifurcate). There are also concentric growth lines. *Terebratella* has a short internal loop, a form of brachidium, on which the lophophore was supported. It has a geological range from Jurassic to Recent. The specimen shown is from Cretaceous strata in France. It grew to a length of about 40mm (1⅝in).

▽ Cyclothyris

An articulate genus with a sub-triangular shell outline, *Cyclothyris* has a pronounced beak containing a small pedicle opening. This can be seen in the specimen on the right. Both valves are convex. The pedicle valve has a broad fold near its anterior margin. The ornamentation consists of many radiating ribs and fine concentric growth lines. The valves have a zig-zag margin in the anterior part where they open, which restricted the size of sediment particles that were able to enter the shell. This feature is often seen in fossil articulate brachiopods, although modern genera lack this shell structure. *Cyclothyris* is found in rocks of Cretaceous age in North America and Europe. It is fossilized in sandstones and limestones.

▽ Torquirhynchia

Both valves of this articulate brachiopod are convex, and the shell has a sub-rounded outline. The beak is strong with a small pedicle opening. The outside surfaces of the shell are ornamented with moderately thick ribs. *Torquirhynchia* lived attached to the sea bed and is found in strata of Upper Jurassic age in Europe and parts of the CIS. The genus grew to about 40mm (1⅝in) diameter.

△ Plectothyris

An articulate genus with a rounded shell margin, *Plectothyris* has a triangular area towards the beak. Both the brachial and pedicle valves are convex. The pedicle opening is large and can be easily seen in the photograph. A characteristic feature of this genus is that the strong ribs are restricted to the margin of the shell; the rest of the shell is smooth. These ribs only developed during adulthood. This brachiopod genus is found in Jurassic strata in Britain, and lived attached to the sea bed individually or in small groups. It grew to about 40mm (1⅝in) in width.

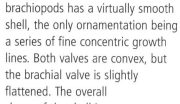

▽ *Pseudoglossothyris*

This genus of large articulate brachiopods has a virtually smooth shell, the only ornamentation being a series of fine concentric growth lines. Both valves are convex, but the brachial valve is slightly flattened. The overall shape of the shell is ovoid. The large pedicle opening can be seen where the larger pedicle valve projects behind the smaller brachial valve. Found in strata, usually limestones, of Jurassic age in Europe, this specimen is from Gloucestershire, UK. When alive this genus was attached by its pedicle to the sea bed, and it grew to a length of about 100mm (4in).

△ *Kingena*

Both valves of this genus of small, globose, articulate brachiopods are strongly convex. The brachial valve is the flatter of the two. The beak is prominent and the pedicle opening large. The rounded shell is smooth apart from a slightly granular texture and faint concentric growth lines. *Kingena* was attached to the sea bed, and is found in various types of rock including limestone and fine-grained detrital rocks such as mudstone. It lived during the Cretaceous period with a worldwide distribution. The pictured specimens are from Lower Cretaceous rocks in Texas, USA. It grew to a maximum diameter of 30mm (1¹/₈in).

▽ *Pygope*

This odd-looking articulate genus is characterized by its triangular outline and central groove. The latter houses an opening from which jets of water were probably expelled. Openings through which the water was taken in are situated on the sides of the shell. In some species, the shell has two lobes. The pedicle opening is large. *Pygope* was attached to the sea bed by its pedicle and is found in various rock types. *Pygope* grew to about 80mm (3¹/₈in) in length, and is found in Jurassic and Cretaceous strata, in Europe. The pictured specimens are from Verona, Italy.

△ *Morrisithyris*

This is an articulate brachiopod with an elongated shell, which is almost wedge-shaped. The characteristic broad, deep fold can be seen in the brachial valve. The shell has little ornament apart from radiating growth lines. The posterior part of the shell is triangular. *Morrisithyris* was attached to the sea bed and grew to about 60mm (2³/₈in) in length. It occurs in strata of Jurassic age in Europe.

6 GRAPTOLITES

Graptolites are a class of colonial marine creatures belonging to the phylum Hemichordata. These delicate fossils inhabited a structure, called a rhabdosome, composed of one or more branches, or stipes. The stipes support small cups known as thecae in which the organisms lived. The appearance of the thecae varies from one genus to another, and these differences are of great value in indentifying the different genera within the class. Some thecae are straight, others curved, hooked or lobate.

TYPES OF GRAPTOLITE

Graptolites are broadly divided into those that have thecae only on one side of the stipe (uniserial) and those with thecae on both sides (biserial). The thecae may form a series of overlapping cups along the length of a stipe. They are connected to each other by the common canal, a thin passage running through the centre of the stipe. The number of thecae varies between genera from only a few to many thousands. The end of a complete stipe has a thin thread-like structure, the nema, extending from it. This may have been an anchoring device. The nema is composed of proteinous material commonly built up in layers. The entire graptolite is rarely more than a few centimetres in length. Among the earliest graptolites was *Dictyonema*, which has many branches and thecae and is referred to as a dendroid graptolite. This genus

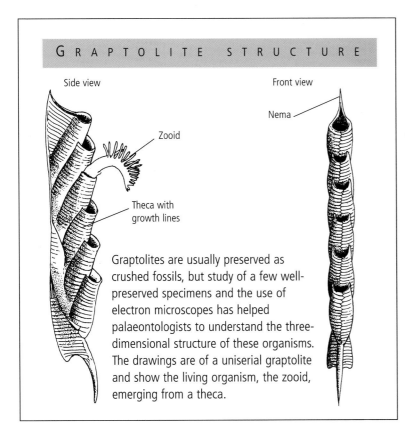

GRAPTOLITE STRUCTURE

Side view

Front view

Nema

Zooid

Theca with
growth lines

Graptolites are usually preserved as crushed fossils, but study of a few well-preserved specimens and the use of electron microscopes has helped palaeontologists to understand the three-dimensional structure of these organisms. The drawings are of a uniserial graptolite and show the living organism, the zooid, emerging from a theca.

◁ *Graptolite site*
Graptolites are typically found in

Lower Palaeozoic black shales such as these in Wales.

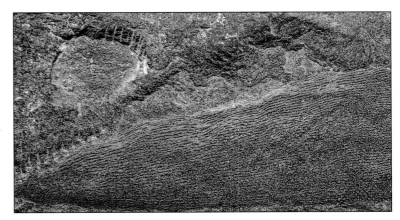

△ *Dictyonema*

This is one of the earliest graptolites and belongs to the dendroid group. Its structure consists of numerous branched stipes joined by transverse dissepiments. When alive, the structure was cone-, or net-shaped, but the fossils are crushed and flat. The stipes are uniserial, carrying thecae only on one side. This graptolite can be from 20 to 250mm ($^3/_4$ to 10in) in length and is found in rocks ranging in age from Cambrian to Carboniferous, worldwide. In Cambrian strata it is found fossilized in fine-grained shales with trilobites such as *Agnostus*, brachiopods and gastropod molluscs. It is one of the few fossils that is found in Ordovician strata in both North America and southern Britain, as there is thought to have been a wide ocean between these land masses and only free-floating or swimming organisms could cross it.

was probably benthonic (sea-bed dwelling), although it may sometimes have attached itself to floating algae. The graptolites with only a few stipes, such as *Monograptus* and *Didymograptus*, are members of the graptoloid group of graptolites. These developed in the Ordovician period and had larger and fewer thecae than the dendroids.

CHARACTERISTICS OF GRAPTOLITE FOSSILS

Graptolite fossils are often found in rocks of Lower Palaeozoic age. They are delicate structures and are only well preserved in fine-grained sediments such as black shale. They are usually preserved as a thin two-dimensional film of carbon or pyrite. However, uncrushed graptolite fossil specimens, found in limestone and chert, have provided material that gives an insight into their true three-dimensional nature. Recent research has shown that the whole of the graptolite structure is resistant to acids like hydrochloric and hydrofluoric acid. This has allowed etching of rocks containing graptolite fossils and their further investigation by electron-microscopy. Because of their rapid evolution and widespread geographical occurrence, certain graptoloid graptolites are used as zone fossils. Long-believed to have become extinct during the Carboniferous period, recent evidence suggests that graptolites may still live in the oceans today.

▽ *Phyllograptus*

This graptolite has four leaf-like stipes. When fossilized they are crushed and usually only two stipes can be distinguished. In life, the four stipes had a cruciform cross-section. The thecae are tube-shaped and usually face upwards.

Phyllograptus belongs to the tetragraptid group. A single structure can be about 30mm (1¹/₈in) long. It is found in Lower Ordovician strata – especially black shales – worldwide. This specimen is from Norway.

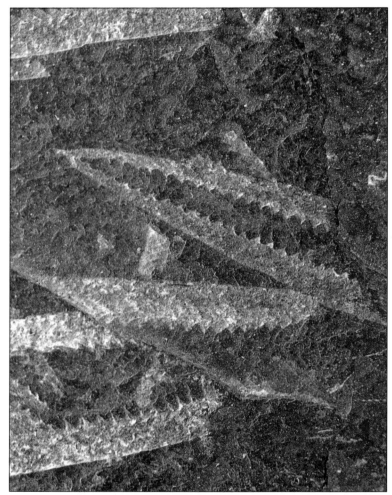

△▷ *Didymograptus*

This genus is characterized by its distinctive 'tuning fork' shape with its two uniserial stipes joined in a V. Some species were pendent, as shown here, with the thecae facing downwards, and others have stipes spread almost in a straight line. The thecae are tube-shaped.

Didymograptus is thought to have been planktonic because it is has a wide distribution and is often found fossilized in large numbers, especially in fine-grained dark mudstones and shales. Such strata are commonly formed in deep-sea environments, but the occurrence of graptolites in these rocks does not

mean that they did not also drift into shallower water. Graptolites may have washed up on the Lower Palaeozoic beaches but the sediment there was too coarse to enable them to be preserved. Some of the largest known graptolites are within this genus, which generally ranges in length from 20 to 600mm

³/₄ to 24in), though specimens 2m (78in) long have been recorded in the United States. *Didymograptus* is found worldwide in rocks of Ordovician age, and a number of species are used as zone fossils for Lower Ordovician strata.

◁▽ *Monograptus*

This common graptolite has a uniserial stipe. There is much variation in the thecae between the different species. Some have simple, others sigmoidal or hook-shaped thecae. The stipes may be straight or coiled. Both types are shown here. A strong virgula supports the rhabdosome in *Monograptus* and this follows the stipe from the base. This genus is found in fine-grained shales and limestones of Silurian and Devonian age, worldwide. It is used as a zone fossil, being common in the British Isles, Norway, Sweden, and the United States, permitting correlation of strata between these places. Graptolites such as *Monograptus* are usually considered to be planktonic organisms that lived in deep-sea conditions. The stipes range from 30 to 750mm (1$\frac{1}{8}$ to 30in) in length.

▷ *Climacograptus*

This is a biserial graptolite with thecae on both sides of its single stipe. These thecae are sigmoidal (S-shaped) and their apertures face upwards. Even with fossils where the graptolite has been crushed, The angular outline of the stipes is quite distinctive. In this genus the nema develops into a virgula, a rod-like structure that reaches into the rhabdosome, and supports the two sets of thecae on the sides of the stipe. A typical specimen is 20mm ($\frac{3}{4}$in) long. This genus is found in strata of Ordovician and Silurian age, worldwide. The Normanskill strata of New York, USA, and the Birkhill shales of southern Scotland are classic localities for this graptolite. It is used as a zone fossil for parts of the Ordovician period.

7 ARTHROPODS

This varied phylum contains many organisms that have a segmented exoskeleton and many legs and other appendages. It includes creatures such as scorpions, spiders, insects, crabs, lobsters and ostracods. Probably the best-known fossil arthropods are the trilobites, of the sub-phylum Trilobita. Other sub-groups include the eurypterids – scorpion-like creatures that grew to great size and terrorized the inhabitants of the Palaeozoic sea bed.

ARTHROPOD CHARACTERISTICS

The typical arthropod exoskeleton can be articulated and the creature may be able to roll up as does the modern woodlouse. As it grows, the arthropod has to shed its skeleton, a process called ecdysis. Largely made of chitin (material similar to that of which our finger nails are made), the arthropod exoskeleton is strengthened with calcite and calcium phosphate and is

▽ *Paradoxides and Peronopsis*
This photograph shows the great diversity to be found among the trilobites. *Paradoxides* can grow to a large size. The specimen seen here, only part of which is shown, is over 300mm (12in) long. It is

from South Wales. The small *Peronopsis*, from Montana, USA, is 8mm (³/₈in) long. Important structural differences between these two genera suggest that they were adapted to very different lifestyles and habitats.

often well preserved as a fossil. Although the soft internal structures of fossil arthropods are not well known, their modern cousins have a well-developed brain and nervous system, joined to the body segments by bundles of nerve fibres.

Arthropods breathe either through the surface of the body or by using gills. Many arthropods – for example, insects and trilobites – have highly developed compound eyes. Other groups have simple eyes. Blood is pumped around the arthropod body by a heart. The phylum is first recorded in Cambrian strata. They have since become a successful and diverse group, adapting to almost every type of environment within the oceans, in fresh water, on land and in the air.

TRILOBITES

This well-known group of extinct organisms occurs in strata as old as the Cambrian period and disappear from the fossil record during the Permian period. One of the problems with tracing the development of these complex organisms is the lack of any fossilized ancestral organism from which the trilobites can be said to have have evolved. It has been suggested that they developed from Pre-Cambrian soft-bodied arthropods that left no trace in rocks of that age. If their time on Earth is a measure of success, then the trilobites rate very highly, the sub-phylum living through more than 300 million years.

Detailed study of their structure and the type of rocks in which they are found as fossils indicates that they probably lived on or near the sea bed. Some crawled along the sea floor and burrowed in the soft sea-bed sediment; others were active swimmers. The segmented trilobite exoskeleton is a complex and well-engineered structure. The name trilobite refers to the three longitudinal lobes of the thorax – a central axis with a

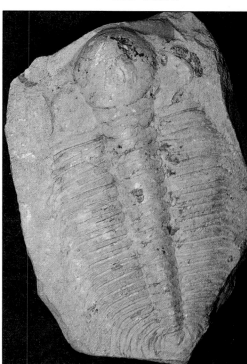

◁ **Ellipsocephalus**
This genus is characterized by a broad, pronounced cephalon which is the widest part of the exoskeleton. It contains a wide, rounded glabella. The tapering thorax has twelve segments. The ridges between the pleurae bifurcate near the margin of the exoskeleton. The eyes are well separated from the glabella. This genus grew to a length of about 35mm (1³/₈in), and occurs in strata of Lower Cambrian age in North America, Europe, North Africa and Australia. The photograph of a specimen from Jince, Czechoslovakia, shows two exoskeletons and the impression of a third, left in the soft Cambrian sea bed.

▷ **Paradoxides**
This well-known trilobite is characterized by a long thorax with over 15 segments, and spinose tapering pleurae. The spines wrap around the thorax and extend around the small, rounded pygidium. The axis of the thorax tapers gradually from the cephalon where it is at its widest. The cephalon has a large glabella and the eyes are large and crescent-shaped. This is one of the largest trilobites, reaching a length of over

500mm (20in). The specimen shown is 85mm (3³/₈in) long and is from Germany. *Paradoxides* occurs in Cambrian strata in North America, South America, North Africa and Europe. It is a zone fossil for parts of the Cambrian period. *Paradoxides* is found fossilized with a variety other organisms, especially those that inhabited moderately shallow marine conditions. These creatures include the brachiopod *Lingulella*, and other trilobites like *Solenopleura*.

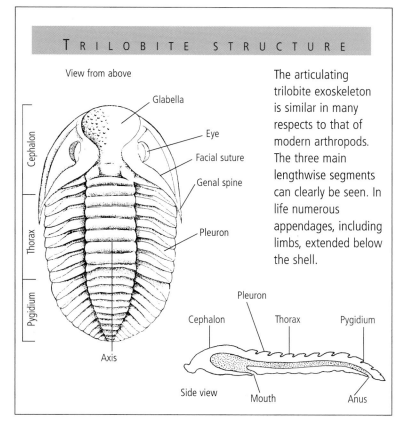

TRILOBITE STRUCTURE

View from above

- Glabella
- Eye
- Facial suture
- Genal spine
- Pleuron
- Cephalon
- Thorax
- Pygidium
- Axis

Side view
- Cephalon
- Pleuron
- Thorax
- Pygidium
- Mouth
- Anus

The articulating trilobite exoskeleton is similar in many respects to that of modern arthropods. The three main lengthwise segments can clearly be seen. In life numerous appendages, including limbs, extended below the shell.

Calymene (page 78-9)
A number of fragmented examples

of this trilobite can be seen in this Silurian limestone.

lateral lobe on each side. These lateral lobes have rib-like segments called pleurae. The prominent head shield, the cephalon, probably contained the centre of the nervous system and its middle section, the glabella, follows the axis of the thorax. Eyes, when present, are on either side of the glabella. These are of compound structure and are composed of calcite. The tail section of the exoskeleton is called the pygidium and generally has a similar structure to that of the thorax. In some genera it has spines and tapers to a long sharp tip.

Like other arthropods, trilobites had to shed their exoskeleton to allow for growth. It is quite possible, therefore, for a single trilobite to produce a number of fossils of its different growth stages. Because of the in-built articulation of the exoskeleton, fossil trilobites are frequently fragmented.

Some trilobite fossils give information about the appendages and soft parts of the organism. *Triarthrus*, from Middle Ordovician rocks of New York, USA, and *Olenoides*

▽ **Eodiscus**

The photograph shows this small trilobite typically preserved as fragmented exoskeletons. The complete trilobite has only three thoracic segments and a horseshoe-shaped cephalon and pygidium of equal size. The narrow glabella is unfurrowed and there is a deep furrow on either side. Both the cephalon and pygidium have a distinct border. This creature was blind and it has been suggested that it burrowed into the sea-bed mud. It is found fossilized in fine-grained sediments deposited on the margins of the continental shelf. *Eodiscus* occurs in rocks of Cambrian age in eastern North America and Europe. The specimen is from South Wales.

△ **Olenellus**

This trilobite has a wide cephalon with genal spines and a glabella with lateral furrows. The large crescent-shaped eyes are attached to the margins of the glabella. The thoracic axis tapers into a tail spine beyond the margin of the small pygidium. The anterior part of the thorax consists of 14 spiny segments, the third pair of pleurae having particularly long spines. The posterior part of the thorax is made of spineless segments. This genus grew to about 80mm (3¹/₈in) in length. It is found in strata of Lower Cambrian age in North America, Greenland and northern Scotland. The specimen shown is from Pennsylvania, USA. The distribution of *Olenellus* is significant. Many trilobites are found in rocks of Lower Cambrian age in Wales, but *Olenellus* is absent from that region. Its presence in northern Scotland suggests that North America, Greenland and northern Scotland were close together during Lower Cambrian times and that a deep ocean, across which *Olenellus* could not migrate, separated these areas from Wales and the rest of Britain.

△ **Ogygopsis**

The genus is characterized by an oval exoskeleton with a thorax that has eight segments. The cephalon contains a deeply furrowed glabella, with eyes about half way along its margin. In complete specimens (the illustrated example is damaged) there are short genal spines. The pygidium has a structure like that of the thorax and has a narrow border. It is longer than the cephalon. The axis tapers gradually from cephalon to pygidium. *Ogygopsis* grew to about 100mm (4in) in length and is found in Middle Cambrian strata in British Columbia, Canada. The specimen shown is from the famous Burgess Shale of that region.

▽ Peronopsis

This tiny trilobite has only two thoracic segments separating its equally-sized pygidium and cephalon. The cephalon has a narrow central glabella with a single furrow. The pygidium has an axis with grooves that extend to the border. The cephalon is similarly bordered. The overall appearance is rather similar to that of *Agnostus* and *Eodiscus*. However, *Agnostus* is differentiated by its two small spines on the pygidium and *Eodiscus* by its three thoracic segments. *Peronopsis* grew to about 8mm (³/₈in) in length and is found fossilized in rocks of Middle Cambrian age in North America, Siberia and Europe. This specimen is from Montana, USA.

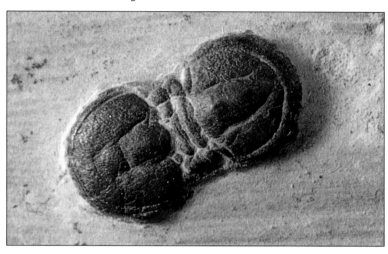

△ Drepanura

This photograph shows a number of fragments of this trilobite – mainly tail segments (pygidia). This part of the creature has two long curved spines and many smaller spines around its border. There is a short, stout axis. The thorax of *Drepanura* has 13 segments and is spinose. The cephalon has small eyes and contains a tapering central glabella, marked laterally by three pairs of furrows. It grew to about 30mm (1¹/₈in) in length, and is found in rocks formed during Middle and Upper Cambrian times. It is especially common in continental shelf limestones, and fossils have been found in eastern Asia and western Europe. The pictured specimen is from China.

THE BURGESS SHALE

In 1909 the American geologist, Charles Doolittle Walcott, who was the secretary of the Smithsonian Institution in Washington, came across a perfect fossil trilobite high in the Rocky Mountains of British Columbia, Canada, in an area of Cambrian strata which he was studying. In 1917 Walcott and his team returned and collected nearly 50,000 fossils. It was not until 1966-7 that the same area was investigated again.

The strata that Walcott discovered are now thousands of metres above sea level. In the Cambrian period this area was well below sea level and there was limestone reef about 150m (500ft) high, at the foot of which muds were forming. It seems that from time to time avalanches of mud carried the organisms that lived on the ledges on the cliff down into the deeper water and they were rapidly entombed in the fine mud at the cliff base.

The organisms fossilized here include arthropods, which crawled on the sea bed, sponges which were attached to the rocks, burrowing worms and swimming chordates. That these disparate creatures are fossilized in the same strata, without traces of burrows or trails, is good evidence for the mud-slide theory, as is the way in which they are preserved, flattened in the mud in a variety of positions. The real importance of the Burgess Shale is that because the sediment was soft and fine grained many soft-bodied creatures have been preserved. This is a rare occurrence and provides information about a wide cross-section of typical Cambrian marine life.

Avalanches of fine-grained sediment swept a wide variety of creatures into the mud at the cliff base.

from the Burgess Shale of Middle Cambrian age in British Columbia, Canada, are sometimes preserved with the appendages intact. These may include antennae, segmented legs and feathery gill-bearing legs. The larval stages of trilobites are not well represented in the fossil record. They are difficult to find because of their small size. Nevertheless, some have been preserved in silica and can therefore be separated from the limestone in which they are embedded by a process of solution. These larvae are called protaspides and consist of a solitary shield-like structure about 1mm (0.04in) long. This has no segmentation and only a faint axis. As the lava matured, the cephalon and pygidium developed along with the segmentation of the thorax. An average trilobite is about 30mm (1⅛in) in length but they can grow to over a metre (39in). The smallest adults reach only 1 or 2mm (0.04 to 0.08in) in length. Fossilized trilobites are found in a great variety of marine sedimentary rocks, including limestones, shales and mudstones.

▷ Solenopleura

This trilobite has a broad cephalon with a wide margin. The glabella is quite narrow with a deep furrow around it. The thorax has 14 segments. Its axis tapers gradually towards the small pygidium. This has seven or eight segments. *Solenopleura* grew to about 50mm (2in) in length, and is found in strata of Middle Cambrian age in North America, New Zealand, Europe and Asia. It occurs in rocks that indicate a shallow marine environment with other trilobites, including *Paradoxides*, and brachiopods such as *Lingulella*.

▷ Meneviella

The photograph shows only a cephalon of this genus. It represents about a quarter of the whole creature. This specimen is of considerable interest because it has radiating striations and indentations on its surface. These features may be related to the trilobite's digestive system. The glabella is narrow and short, and its margins are broken by weak furrows. This trilobite grew to about 60mm (2⅜in) in length and is found in Middle Cambrian strata in eastern North America, Britain, Denmark and Asia. The pictured specimen is

▽ Elrathia

This common genus from North America is characterized by a wide-margined cephalon that is much wider than the thorax. The cephalon has short spines that curve over the first two or three thoracic segments. The glabella is short and ovoid. The eyes are joined by small ridges in some species. The thoracic axis tapers gradually towards the small pygidium. There are 13 segments in the thorax. *Elrathia* grew to about 30mm (1⅛in) in length and is found – often in great numbers – in Middle Cambrian strata in North America. The specimen shown is from the Wheeler formation of Utah, USA.

◁ Agnostus

This diminutive trilobite has only two thoracic segments. The relatively large cephalon and pygidium are of approximately equal size, and have broad borders. The glabella is narrow and has a single furrow. The pygidium may have two small spines. There are no eyes in the usual place and this genus is usually considered to be sightless. *Agnostus* is found worldwide in strata of Upper Cambrian age, where it is used as a zone fossil. The specimen shown is from Vastergotland, Sweden. This genus probably lived in moderately deep marine conditions, on the deeper parts of the continental shelf. Some palaeontologists believe that *Agnostus* lived on or near the sea floor, while others have suggested that it may have lived with floating algae.

◁ **Trinucleus**

The most typical feature of this genus is the very large cephalon and rounded glabella. The cephalon has a pitted border, which may have been a mechanism for detecting water pressure. The semicircular shape of the cephalon is emphasized by the long genal spines extending far beyond the pygidium. These are, however, absent in this example. *Trinucleus* has no eyes, and the glabella is convex with two to three pairs of deep furrows. The short thorax has only six segments, and the pygidium is almost triangular in outline. This genus grew to about 30mm (1¹/₈in) in length and it is found in rocks of Ordovician age in Britain and Russia. The specimen shown is from Wales. *Trinucleus* occurs in fine-grained sediments of the type often associated with moderately deep marine conditions. It is often found with other trilobites such as *Ogygiocarella* and brachiopods like *Lingulella*.

▽ **Ogyginus**

This trilobite has a cephalon and pygidium of about the same size. The large glabella reaches to the margin of the exoskeleton and has prominent eyes on either side. Genal spines extend a short way along the thorax. These are often broken off before fossilization, but can be seen in the specimen illustrated. There are eight segments in the thorax. *Ogyginus* grew to a length of about 40mm (1⁵/₈in) and is found in Ordovician strata in Europe. This specimen is from Wales.

◁ **Ogygiocarella**

There has been much confusion over the name of this trilobite. It has been – and still is by some authorities – called *Ogigia* and *Ogigiocaris*. It is characterized by a large cephalon from which extend long genal spines. In this specimen the cephalon is fragmented. The glabella, visible in the photograph, narrows as it meets the exoskeleton margin. The eyes are crescent-shaped. The thorax has eight segments and is relatively short with parallel sides. The large pygidium is broad-margined and almost triangular in outline. It has a narrow, tapering axis. *Ogygiocarella* reached over 80mm (3¹/₈in) in length, and is found in Ordovician strata in Europe and South America.

TRILOBITE ENROLLING

One of the specimens of *Calymene* shown on the facing page is in the enrolled position. Many genera are found fossilized like this including *Encrinurus*, *Illaenus* and *Phacops*. The exact purpose of coiling the exoskeleton is uncertain, but a number of suggestions have been made. Some trilobite fossils have been found that show damage probably made by a predator. In Palaeozoic times the seas contained large nautiloids, and later, fish. Both could have eaten trilobites, and large trilobites may have preyed on smaller species. By enrolling, a trilobite could have been taking on a defensive posture which provided protection for its soft ventral surface. However, an enrolled trilobite may also have been easier to swallow than one with its exoskeleton extended! If the trilobite enrolled while it was swimming this would cause a sudden descent. This could have been used as a way of avoiding predators.

It is possble that trilobites may have remained enrolled for quite some time. Some genera even have structures on the exoskeleton that allow the cephalon and pygidium to be linked together. If this position was held for lengthy spans of time then what would be the reason? It has been argued that trilobites could slow their body functions down, possibly when food became scarce, and an enrolled position may have conserved energy at such a time. They may have adopted the posture when the conditions on or near the sea bed became unfavourable or threatening. Certainly some modern arthropods with similar segmented structure (the pillbug or woodlouse, for example) enroll when attacked or when at rest. When drawing analogies like this care must be taken, however, and the very different environments in which these modern creatures live, when compared with the trilobites, may make the comparison invalid.

▽ **Illaenus**
A characteristic feature of this trilobite genus is its broad, smooth cephalon and pygidium. These parts are of about equal size and have a semicircular outline. The glabella is indistinct and there are large crescent-shaped eyes. The thorax has ten segments. *Illaenus* grew to about 50mm (2in) in length and is found in rocks of Ordovician age, worldwide. The pictured specimen is from Oporto, Portugal. Like many modern arthropods, this genus may have lived in the mud on the sea bed, possibly with its large eyes just above the sediment surface.

◁ **Triarthrus**
This genus has a semicircular cephalon with wide borders and a segmented glabella. The eyes are small. The thorax has 12 to 16 segments, and a central axis that tapers gradually and extends into the pygidium. This has five segments. *Triarthrus* is of considerable interest because specimens in which the soft parts have been preserved have been found in North America. These include walking and gill-bearing limbs, antennae and other appendages. It grew to about 30mm (1 1/8in) in length and is found in Ordovician strata, worldwide. This specimen is from New York, USA.

◁ *Ampyx*

The pictured specimen shows how a trilobite exoskeleton breaks up on the sea bed. The cephalon has almost separated from the thorax. This genus has six thoracic segments, and the cephalon and pygidium are of about equal size. In complete specimens a long spine projects from the glabella. There are no eyes on the cephalon. *Ampyx* is a small trilobite that grew to about 15mm ($^5/_8$in) in length. However, in spinose species, the anterior and genal spines could be three times the body length. It is found in rocks of Middle Ordovician age in North America and Europe.

▽▷ *Calymene*

Two specimens of this common trilobite are pictured. One (below) is enrolled. The genus has a near-triangular cephalon, which contains a large glabella. This has two rounded extensions on each side and a deep furrow surrounds it. The posterior margin of the cephalon forms the widest part of the exoskeleton. The thoracic axis tapers only in its last few segments. There are 12 to 13 thoracic segments. The six-segmented pygidium tapers rapidly, but has a structure that is otherwise similar to that of the thorax. This genus grew to about 100mm (4in) in length and is found in strata of Silurian and Devonian age in North America, South America, Australia and Europe. Both specimens shown are from Shropshire, UK. This trilobite is found in rocks that indicate shallow-water, continental shelf deposition – especially limestones – and calcareous shales. The other fossils in these strata include corals, various brachiopods, algae and bryozoans. The presence of corals in this environment may suggest warm, shallow conditions, but an active creature such as *Calymene*, which could swim near or creep along the sea bed, was not restricted to this environment. Indeed, *Calymene* is also found in deep-water strata.

▽ **Onnia**

The pictured specimen, found in Wales, is of an isolated cephalon of this genus. It is very large and the main characteristics can clearly be seen. There is a perforated border, not unlike that of *Trinucleus*, and the glabella is prominent and rounded. It has been suggested that the distinctive border structure may have been able to detect movement of water currents or subtle changes in water pressure. Long genal

spines (not present here) extend well beyond the pygidium. The thorax of this genus was short, with only five segments and a small triangular pygidium. The genus grew to a length of about 20mm ($^3/_4$in). It occurs in Middle and Upper Ordovician rocks, in Europe, North Africa and South America. In some regions, *Onnia* is found in deep-water strata with other trilobites and brachiopods.

△ **Trimerus**

This trilobite is characterized by a triangular cephalon without eyes and a weakly developed glabella that appears as an almost square convex area in the cephalon. The thorax is unusual in that while it is typically segmented, there is no division into central and lateral lobes. Its segments are very smooth. The pygidium is triangular,

with an axial lobe, and it tapers to a narrow point. The smoothness of the exoskeleton and the lack of eyes has led to the suggestion that this trilobite burrowed in the mud on the sea bed. It grew to about 200mm (8in) in length, and is found in strata of Silurian and Devonian age, worldwide. The pictured specimen is from Shropshire, UK.

▷ **Dalmanites**

This genus has a large semicircular cephalon from which extend genal spines (one of which is visible in this specimen) that reach beyond the third thoracic segment. The glabella widens towards the front. The thorax has 11 segments, and the tapering axis continues through the pygidium. This is quite small and triangular in shape. Missing from this example, there is a long tail spine in some specimens. A shorter spine may also be present on the anterior margin of the cephalon. These spines may have been for support on the sea-bed sediment, or for stirring up the loose sediment to find food. The large eyes on either side of the glabella extend above the cephalon. This may have given *Dalmanites* vision through 360 degrees. This genus grew to about 80mm (3$^1/_8$in)

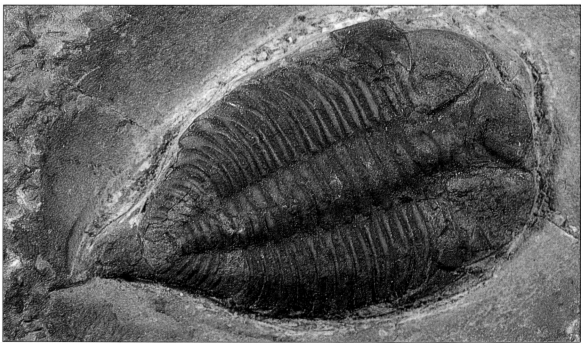

in length and is found in strata of Silurian and Devonian age in North America, Europe, parts of the CIS and Australia. It commonly occurs in Silurian reef limestones where it is associated with many shallow marine organisms including corals, brachiopods, and orthocone nautiloids.

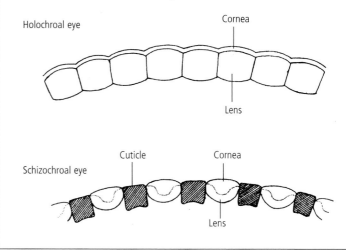

Trilobite eyes

In common with many modern arthropods, many trilobites possessed compound eyes. These are often perfectly preserved in fossils, possibly because they were made of calcite, a mineral which is common in sedimentary environments. These trilobite eyes consist of a large number of calcite lenses, which are often polygonal or rounded in shape. Originally palaeontologists thought that the calcite material in trilobite eyes was a replacement mineral formed during fossilization. Research has shown, however, that calcite has certain optical properties and light will pass along one of the crystallographic axes as easily as through glass. It was also found that this axis in the calcite crystals was at right angles to the surface of the lenses in the eyes. Such an arrangement of the calcite could not have occurred during fossilization.

Eye structures

There are two types of trilobite eyes. Holochroal eyes have virtually polygonal lenses that are joined together and covered by a single cornea. There can be several thousand lenses in this structure, and most trilobites with eyes have this system. Schizochroal eyes are found only in one group of trilobites, the sub-order Phacopina, which includes *Phacops*. These eyes are more sophisticated, and have lenses that are separated from one another by a cuticle, each lens having its own cornea. It has been shown that these lenses contain a wavy surface within them that corrects any differences in the light passing through the upper and lower surface of the lens to give a sharply focused image. It has been suggested that trilobites with these eyes may have lived in dark areas or were active at night.

Eye placement and size

Compound eyes of both types allow a creature to detect even small movements, and enhance its effectiveness at food-gathering and its ability to perceive threats to its safety. The eyes of trilobites are usually near to the margins of the glabella, which is thought to have been the centre of the nervous system. Some genera had their eyes towards the front of the cephalon, others carried eyes on stalks, possibly so that the animal could lie in the mud and still see.

Some trilobite eyes are small, others are of great size. Some species lacked eyes of any kind. This sightlessness is thought to be an evolutionary development from forms that had eyes. Perhaps their eyes became redundant because they were burrowers with no need to see.

▽△ **Phacops**
This trilobite is characterized by the indentations on the glabella. *Phacops* has large kidney-shaped eyes and rounded genal angles, without spines. The thorax has 11 segments and a gradually tapering axis. The pygidium is small and usually curved. Specimens of *Phacops* frequently have well-preserved eyes and also are often found enrolled. The genus usually grew to about 60mm (2³/₈in) in length, but specimens of the species *Phacops rana* from North America can be as long as 150mm (6in). *Phacops* occurs in strata of Silurian and Devonian age in North America, North Africa and Europe. In Devonian strata, *Phacops* is found in sediments deposited well away from the coastline.

▷ **Leonaspis**

This genus has spines growing from most of the thoracic segments, the cephalon and the pygidium. The cephalon is relatively large with robust genal spines. These wrap around the thorax to about the sixth thoracic segment. The glabella has furrows at its anterior end, and it reaches to the denticulate (finely toothed) margin of the cephalon. Small eyes are positioned on either side of the glabella. The thorax, which has eight to ten segments, has long, posteriorly curved spines from every segment, and the axis tapers gradually towards the pygidium. This is a small structure with only one pair of large spines, and two smaller pairs of spines. It has an almost rectangular anterior margin. *Leonaspis* grew to about 20mm (³/₄in) length, and it is found in rocks formed on the continental shelves during the Silurian and Devonian periods, in North America, South America, Australia, Asia and Europe.

▽ **Encrinurus**

Encrinurus is characterized by its nodular cephalon. This is divided into three distinct parts: the central glabella, which widens anteriorly, and the two cheeks on either side.

The eyes are above the cephalon on short stalks. These can be seen in this specimen, although they are slightly damaged. The thorax has 11 to 12 segments. The photograph shows the positive fossil (left) and the mould it has left in the rock (right). This genus grew to about 80mm (3¹/₈in) in length, and is found in continental shelf strata of Ordovician, Silurian and Devonian age, worldwide.

▷ **Bumastus**

This trilobite is characterized by the smoothness of its cephalon and pygidium. The cephalon is large without a definite glabella. The eyes are placed in the faint grooves that mark the margins of the glabella. The thorax has ten narrow segments and a wide central axis. The pygidium lacks segmentation and is a similar size to the cephalon. *Bumastus* is commonly fragmented before fossilization. It grew to about 100mm (4in) in length and is found in Silurian rocks in North America and Europe.

▽ **Acidaspis**

This trilobite has spines from the cephalon and most of its segments. The cephalon is relatively large with a front margin of small spines. Unfortunately these features cannot be seen in this specimen, which is broken. *Acidaspis* has stout genal spines that extend to about the sixth thoracic segment. The glabella, which has eyes on either side, reaches to the anterior margin of the cephalon. This genus has an oval thorax with a tapering axis. A long, curved spine emerges from each of the ten thoracic segments. The pygidium is small, with a short spine on its first segment and longer ones on the second segment. There are four comb-like spines at the posterior end of the pygidum. *Acidaspis* grew to about 30mm (1⅛in) in length, and is found in Ordovician to Middle Devonian strata in North America and Europe.

▷ **Proetus**

Proetus has a large rounded cephalon with a bulging glabella. This is smooth and has the eyes set on either side of it. The cephalon has a pronounced margin and curves around the first two thoracic segments. The thorax is without spines and has a broad axis. There are up to 12 thoracic segments. The almost semicircular pygidium is large, with an axis that ends before the posterior border. This genus grew to a length of about 30mm (1⅛in), and is found in Ordovician to Carboniferous strata, worldwide. This Devonian specimen is from Germany.

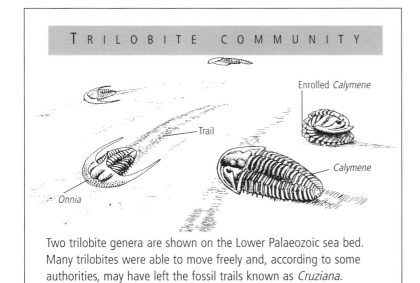

TRILOBITE COMMUNITY

Enrolled *Calymene*

Trail

Calymene

Onnia

Two trilobite genera are shown on the Lower Palaeozoic sea bed. Many trilobites were able to move freely and, according to some authorities, may have left the fossil trails known as *Cruziana*.

◁ **Scutellum**

The photograph shows only the pygidium of this trilobite. This genus is unusual because it has a series of radiating ribs on the pygidium. These divide from where it joins the thorax. The pygidium is about 30mm (1¹/₈in) long. Complete specimens have a cephalon with an oval outline and a glabella that widens anteriorly. The eyes are complex, with over 4,000 individual lenses being found in some species. The thorax has ten spinose segments. The genus is found in Silurian and Devonian rocks, worldwide. This specimen was found in Devonian strata near Prague, Czechoslovakia, where the trilobite occurs in great masses in shallow-water limestones.

▷ **Eocyphinium**

This trilobite belongs to a group often referred to as Phillipsia. Only the pygidium is shown. This has a typical three-lobed structure, a triangular outline and a tapering axis. In complete specimens the cephalon is large and genal spines wrap closely around the first three thoracic segments. There is a prominent border to the cephalon and the glabella is parallel sided. The eyes are away from the glabella. The thorax usually has ten segments and is wide with a narrow, tapering axis. *Eocyphinium* is found in Europe in Carboniferous strata and grew to about 25mm (1in) in length.

◁ **Cromus**

Two pygidia of this small trilobite can be seen in this specimen of limestone. This genus is characterized by a cephalon with short genal spines and a definite border. The glabella has four pairs of lateral furrows and widens slightly towards the front of the cephalon. The eyes are close to the glabella. The thorax has ten segments. The pygidium tapers rapidly and has a rounded surface. It has 10 to 16 segments. This trilobite is found in Silurian rocks in Europe.

OTHER ARTHROPODS

Although the trilobites may be the best-known members of the phylum Arthropoda found as fossils, there are many other arthropods that have been fossilized, and some of these reached an immense size. Such arthropods include ancient crabs, lobsters, scorpions, eurypterids and even insects. There are many similarities between these creatures and the trilobites. They have a segmented exoskeleton that protects the body. Many of them can swim efficiently and others crawl on the sea bed. They live in many different marine and non-marine habitats, and are found in a wide variety of sedimentary rocks.

Some of the most delicate arthropod fossils are of insects. These can be preserved in a variety of ways. The trapping of insects in the resin from pine trees, which hardens to amber, is well known. But many insects have also been preserved in the famous fine-grained limestones of Solnhofen in southern Germany. Here, mainly because of the fineness of the sediment, mayflies, dragonflies, cockroaches, water skaters, locusts and water scorpions of Jurassic age have been fossilized. In the Lower Carboniferous strata of southern Scotland fine-grained limestones have preserved scorpions and delicate harvestmen.

△ **Euproops**
This genus belongs to the subclass Xiphosura, which includes the king crabs. *Euproops* resembles the modern horse-shoe crab, and its structure is reminiscent of the trilobites. There is a cephalon, with genal spines and an extension of the thoracic axis. The thorax is segmented, and has webbed spines along its margins. The pygidium is small and spinose. Growing to about 40mm (1⅝in) in length, *Euproops* occurs in Upper Carboniferous and Permian strata in North America and Europe.

▽ **Waterstonella**
This dark slab of Carboniferous shale from Granton Harbour near Edinburgh, Scotland, contains numerous remains of a small crustacean. The order to which these creatures belong contains segmented organisms not unlike small shrimps with an exoskeleton consisting of a thorax and tail. Its head has eyes and long antennae. In some species, the tail expands laterally into a fan shape. The fossils shown here are typical and very fragmented. Such small arthropods lived in marine or brackish water conditions. These arthropods occur in Lower Carboniferous rocks, worldwide.

△ **Euphorberia**
This creature belongs to the superclass Myrapoda. These thin elongated arthropods are mainly land-dwelling. Modern millipedes and centipedes belong to this group. The oldest fossil millipedes are from rocks of Upper Silurian age in Scotland and are often found in Carboniferous strata. The segmented body and thin limbs of this genus can be easily seen in the pictured specimen, preserved in an ironstone nodule. In complete specimens the head is wider than the thorax. *Euphorberia* lived in the swamp forests of the Upper Carboniferous period. It is only rarely that land-dwelling arthropods such as this are well fossilized, because the likelihood of being buried in sediment soon after death is less than for arthropods living in water. This genus grew to about 80mm (3⅛in) in length. *Euphorberia* is found in rocks of Carboniferous age in North America and Europe. The specimen shown is from Staffordshire, UK.

▽ **Mesolimulus**

A 'king crab' which has a number of identifying characteristics, the exoskeleton of this genus is that of a typical arthropod, with cephalon, thorax and pygidium. The cephalon is large and semicircular with genal spines extending around the anterior part of the thorax. There are two kidney-shaped eyes, and the cephalon has a pronounced border. A slender, pointed extension of the axis reaches into the cephalon. The thorax is short and triangular, and the pygidium ends in a long tail spine. There are six pairs of limbs beneath the anterior part of the body. Of these the posterior five pairs are for walking. The anterior pair has large pincers. Many related modern genera live close to the Atlantic coast of North America, in the mangrove swamps of Southeast Asia and in the Indian Ocean. They feed on vegetation and smaller crustaceans. Fossil examples may have had a similar way of life. The genus grew to about 250mm (10in) in length, and is found in Mesozoic rocks in Europe. This example is from the *plattenkalk* limestones of Solnhofen, in Germany, where many fine examples have been found.

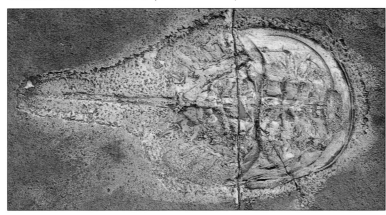

△ **Aeger**

This is a genus of decapod crustaceans which, like *Mesolimulus*, is from the Solnhofen limestones of Germany. The exoskeleton is very thin and not often fossilized. It is composed of chitin and calcareous material both of which may break down unless burial is rapid. Unless the sediment is fine grained, details may not be recorded. Both these requirements were fulfilled at Solnhofen in Jurassic times. *Aeger* has an exoskeleton that is compressed laterally and many slender appendages. Long feelers extend from the head. (These have been broken off from the pictured fossil.) The front pair of limbs are covered with bristles. This genus has been found in Upper Triassic to Upper Jurassic strata, and grew to about 80mm (3¹/₈in) in length.

The limestones of Solnhofen in southern Germany are famous for their well-preserved fossils. The limestones, which split easily into flat sheets and slabs, are called *plattenkalk*, or 'plate limestone'. Pure limestones are not the only rocks; there are also alternating layers of clay-rich limestone. The pure limestones may be 300mm (12in) thick and the interbedded clay-limestones are about 30mm (1¹/₈in) thick. Fossils are not especially common in the Solnhofen strata, but those that are found, including land-dwelling and marine organisms, are exceptionally well preserved. They include many soft-bodied and delicate organisms such as plants, jellyfish, worms, insects and other arthropods, as well as molluscs, fish and land-dwelling vertebrates.

The most celebrated fossils from these rocks are of the early bird *Archaeopteryx*. The first fragment of this genus to be found was a single feather that came to light in 1860. This amazing discovery was followed in 1861 by that of a skeleton with feathers. Since then six specimens have been found. The origins and evolution of this creature are hotly debated. It has many reptilian features, such as its pelvis, and has three clawed fingers on its hands, but does not have the keeled sternum that is typical of birds. This fossil is best considered as a bird with many reptile-like characteristics.

The *plattenkalk* was formed in a warm lagoon that was probably separated from the open sea by a sand bar or barrier-reef of coral. From time to time, perhaps during storms, the sea washed into the lagoon. Conditions in the lagoon itself were hostile to life, because of the saltiness and warmth of the water, and the organisms that were carried into the lagoon from the sea or by river systems quickly died. Among the few organisms that were able to endure these conditions were bacteria and algae. These built up mounds in the lagoon and divided it into discrete regions. Certain molluscs such as bivalves existed floating attached to algae.

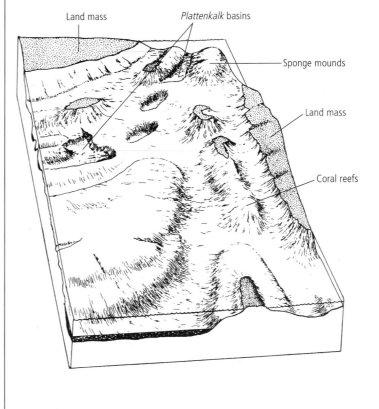

Land mass   *Plattenkalk* basins   Sponge mounds   Land mass   Coral reefs

△ Glyphea

This arthropod is a member of the Decapoda, a group that includes lobsters and shrimps. It has five pairs of limbs, which are only rarely fossilized. The exoskeleton, or carapace, has a rough, granulose surface. The head has eyes and segmented feelers. *Glyphea* grew to about 45mm (1³/₄in) in length. It occurs in Triassic, Jurassic and Cretaceous strata and has been found in North America, Europe, Greenland, East Africa and Australia. The pictured specimen is from North Yorkshire, UK. *Glyphea* is often associated with a trace fossil burrow called *Thalassinoides*. It is possible that *Glyphea* made these burrows, which also contain fossilized fecal pellets, known as *Favreina*, which have been attributed to *Glyphea*.

△ Euestheria

On first inspection, the carapace of this arthropod looks very like a bivalve mollusc shell. It has a rounded shape and there are concentric growth lines, easily seen in this photograph. These result from moulting (ecdysis). *Euestheria* belongs to the Branchiopoda, a class that includes both shelled and unshelled creatures. This genus lived in non-marine waters, and ranges from the Lower Devonian to Recent, with a worldwide distribution. This specimen is from the Isle of Skye, Scotland, where the genus occurs in non-marine strata of Middle Jurassic age, with other non-marine creatures, such as the molluscs *Viviparus* and *Unio*.

△ Zanthopsis

This fossil from the Oligocene rocks of the Lincoln Creek Formation, Washington, USA, is enclosed in a nodular mass. The claws can be distinguished towards the top of the picture.

△ Archaeogeryon

This genus of crab is in many respects similar to modern genera. Such fossils are found in rocks formed in shallow marine conditions. It has a tough carapace with a rough surface and many small raised markings, which covers the softer body. In some fossils the carapace is crushed and only the limbs become fossilized. *Archaeogeryon* is found in Tertiary rocks, worldwide. The pictured specimen is from Miocene strata in South America. This crab grew to a width of about 100mm (4in).

ARTHROPOD BURROW

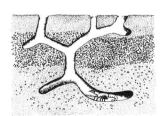

The trace fossil *Thalassinoides* often occurs in Jurassic sediments. It is generally thought to be the burrows of the arthropod *Glyphea*. Fossils of *Glyphea* have been found near the burrows.

LOWER DEVONIAN FRESH-WATER COMMUNITY

The Lower Devonian period saw the evolution of the first complex fresh-water ecosystems, which included fish, arthropods and plants.

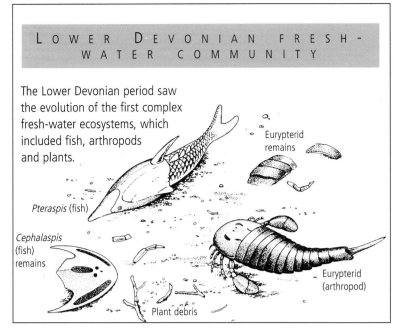

Pteraspis (fish)

Cephalaspis (fish) remains

Plant debris

Eurypterid remains

Eurypterid (arthropod)

◁△▽ *Pterygotus*

This organism is in the subclass Euripterida. They are slender, segmented creatures resembling scorpions. The thorax has broad segments and tapers gradually to a tail which may have small spines on the margins of its segments. The head has a pair of long, flexible appendages equipped with strong claws, presumably for grasping prey. There are three pairs of smaller limbs, possibly for walking and a large pair of paddle-like limbs situated near the point where the thorax and head meet. Its large eyes are situated near the anterior margin of the head. It is generally thought that these creatures, which grew to over 2 metres (78in) in length, were fierce predators, living on or swimming near the sea bed. They were alive during the Ordovician, Silurian and Devonian periods, and their fossils are found in North America, South America, Europe, Asia and Australia, in marine and brackish water sediments. The specimens shown are a whole individual, about 200mm (8in) in length (above left), a single claw (left) and detail of the scales on a fragment of one segment of a thorax (top).

◁▽ **Hoploparia**

As with fossil crabs, fossil lobsters have many features which are very similar to those of modern genera. Here the segmented body and slender appendages can be distinguished, especially in the larger specimen. Both the specimens shown are enclosed in nodular iron-rich concretions, that give good three-dimensional preservation. Such fossils are reasonably common in shallow-water marine strata, because the tough exoskeleton is easily preserved. This genus is found in Tertiary rocks, worldwide.

▽ **Libellula**

In exceptional circumstances even delicate insects can be preserved. This is a dragonfly larva, fossilized in very fine Miocene limestone at Piedmont, Italy. Whole adult dragonflies of related genera are found in the Solnhofen *plattenkalk*. The dragonfly larva is aquatic and it is therefore more likely that it will be preserved than an adult insect. In this example, the segmented thorax, appendages and small head are visible. The specimen is 15mm (⁵/₈in) long. The genus occurs in strata of Triassic to Recent in age, worldwide.

▽ **Cybister**

This beetle carapace has been preserved in a tarry carbonaceous deposit. The detail of the wing cases and of the head are clearly seen. This fossil is made of original material, and there have been no chemical changes. It is from Pleistocene strata in California, USA, and is 40mm (1⁵/₈ in) long. Fossils that have modern relatives, like this example, are of great value in reconstructing past environments.

8 MOLLUSCS

The phylum Mollusca is one of the most successful and diverse. Its fossilized representatives first appear in strata of Cambrian age. These are well developed organisms and presumably must have evolved from Pre-Cambrian ancestors. Some experts have suggested that these primitive ancestral molluscs were segmented worm-like creatures. Others prefer to regard the ancestral mollusc as a creature not unlike the modern Monoplacophora.

According to this latter view, early molluscs would have had a simple, possibly cone-shaped, shell and a large 'head-foot' that protruded from the base. However, until fossil evidence is forthcoming, this original mollusc remains a matter of conjecture. There are a number of important features that characterize molluscs. These are not always present in the different classes because there is such diversity between them, but nevertheless they are molluscan traits. Many have a shell which, in the majority of genera, is external. The body tends to be surrounded by a slippery outer skin or mantle. The shape of the shell varies enormously between the genera and classes, and because many molluscs are unable to move very far or fast, they are designed to suit their environment.

CLASSES OF MOLLUSCS

The classes that are important as fossils are the bivalves (sometimes called the Pelecypoda or Lamellibranchia), the cephalopods, the gastropods and the scaphopods. The bivalves have a shell composed of two, usually similar, valves. The class includes cockles, oysters, mussels and clams. The gastropods include snails and slugs that may live in the sea, in fresh water, on land and even in trees. These are discussed in Chapter 9. The cephalopods, discussed in Chapter 10, are a class containing active swimming molluscs, often held within beautifully constructed plano-spiral shells. Squid, octopus, cuttlefish, nautiloids, argonauts and the extinct ammonoids belong to this class. A less well-known class that is sometimes found fossilized are the scaphopods – the slender tusk shells. The two other classes in the phylum, the Monoplacophora and the Amphineura, are rare as fossils, and are not therefore discussed here.

THE IMPORTANCE OF MOLLUSCS

Fossil molluscs are of great use to the palaeontologist. Many of them, especially the bivalves, which are very particular about water depth, sea-floor material and salinity, are useful in palaeo-environment reconstruction. The ammonoids are classic zone fossils allowing relative dating and correlation of strata, and the gastropods are also of value for dating rocks though not in such a widespread manner as the ammonoids.

◁△ **Arnioceras**
This magnificent bedding plane from Lower Jurassic strata in

Dorset, UK, is crowded with shells of this cephalopod mollusc.

BIVALVE MOLLUSCS

This class first appears in Cambrian rocks and is still very common today. Tellins, oysters, mussels, cockles and clams are all bivalve molluscs. Their characteristic two-part shell is composed of calcium carbonate, usually in the form of aragonite, although some species have calcite, and it has a thin coating of protein. The valves are usually symmetrical and are mirror images of each other, with the plane of symmetry passing between the valves.

The two valves are held together and opened by a mechanism consisting of a combination of muscles, ligaments and teeth. The teeth are projections of the valves, which fit into corresponding sockets in the other valve. Together they form a hinge near to the beak-shaped umbo. There are commonly two adductor muscles, although some genera only have one. These muscles hold the two valves together and when they relax, the horny ligament near the hinge teeth opens the valves slightly. Dead shells often become disarticulated because of the relaxation and decay of the adductor muscles.

INSIDE THE VALVES

The position and size of the adductor muscles can be judged from the muscle scars on the inside of the valves. These rounded impressions are often visible in fossils, and occur on the anterior and posterior parts of the valves. When two muscle scars are present they are usually joined by a faint line – the pallial line – which marks the margin of the attachment of the mantle inside the shell. This is a fleshy envelope which contains the soft body of the bivalve and secretes the shell tissue. The pallial line may have an indentation, called the pallial sinus. The presence of this feature indicates that the bivalve in question was a burrower. This is known because the sinus marks the position of the retractor muscles needed to pull the large siphons (tubular organs through which water passes), which a burrower needed, into the shell. A bivalve takes in water along with the microscopic organisms that are its food through an inhalent siphon. The tiny particles are trapped on mucus-covered gills and passed to the mouth. Another, exhalent, siphon removes waste matter.

◁ **Mass of bivalves**
Here a collection of small bivalve molluscs have been fossilized together.

▷ **Posidonia**
This genus of bivalve mollusc has an almost circular shell outline. The dorsal margin (where the umbo is situated) is straight. The valves are flat and thin, and the umbo only weakly developed. The posterior of the shell is slightly elongated. The ornamentation on the outside of the shell consists of concentric growth lines and narrow ribs. This genus grew to about 35mm (1³/₈in) in diameter, and is found all over the world in strata of the Carboniferous to Jurassic periods. *Posidonia* may have lived attached to sea-weed or floating wood.

△ **Dunbarella**
The valves of this bivalve are thin-shelled and almost round. The hinge line is straight. Ribs radiate to the shell margin from the pointed umbo. The concentric growth lines are faint. Winged extensions are visible on either side of the umbo. This genus grew to about 40mm (1⁵/₈in) in diameter. It is found in strata of the Carboniferous period in North America and Europe. *Dunbarella* often occurs in black shales, formed in relatively deep marine conditions, along with species of goniatites and other bivalves, including *Posidonia*. *Dunbarella* may have swum freely, above the oxygen-lacking sea bed.

THE BIVALVE ENVIRONMENT

Bivalves have become adapted to many environments – both marine and freshwater. Some bivalves, like oysters, are permanently attached to the sea bed, while others, like *Mya*, burrow deeply into the sediment and can be found fossilized in their burrows. Some members of the genus *Pecten* can swim by flapping their flattened valves together, and many bivalves move slowly across the sea bed by pushing themselves along with a tough, fleshy, tongue-like foot which projects between the valves. Bivalves are very common fossils and today there are over 10,000 species. They are usually quite small – about 10 to 100mm ($^3/_8$ to 4in) in diameter – but there are some enormous bivalves that reach 1500mm (60in) across.

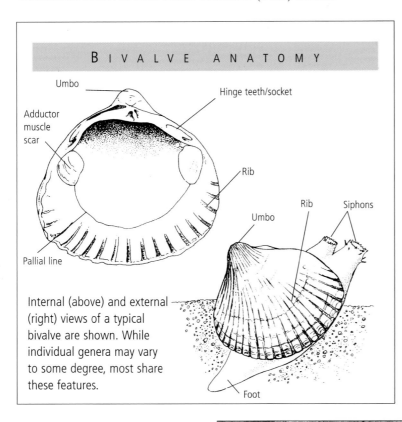

BIVALVE ANATOMY

Umbo
Hinge teeth/socket
Adductor muscle scar
Rib
Rib
Siphons
Umbo
Pallial line
Foot

Internal (above) and external (right) views of a typical bivalve are shown. While individual genera may vary to some degree, most share these features.

▽ **Anthraconauta**
The genus is characterized by a thin elongated shell covered with concentric growth lines. It lived in the non-marine streams and rivers of the vast Carboniferous deltas. The photograph shows a dark shale bedding plane crowded with masses of shells. *Anthraconauta* is one of the genera used to subdivide and correlate the coal-bearing rocks of Carboniferous age. It grew to about 50mm (2in) in length, and occurs in Carboniferous and Permian strata in Europe.

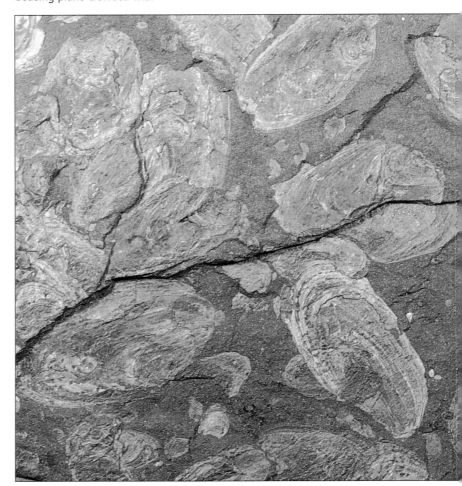

▷ **Carbonicola**
This bivalve has a sub-triangular shell outline. There is a reasonably pronounced posterior elongation of the shell. This has concentric growth lines, but no ribs. *Carbonicola* moved through and into the mud by pushing with its fleshy foot. It lived in the lakes and distributary channels of the deltas of the coal-forming forests of the Carboniferous period. It is associated with other bivalves such as *Anthraconauta*. *Carbonicola* occurs only in Upper Carboniferous rocks in Europe and Russia and has been used to correlate the coal-bearing strata. It grew to about 60mm (2$^3/_8$in) in length.

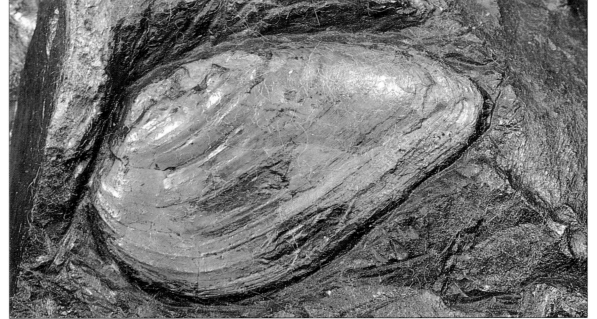

▷ *Schizodus*

This genus has a smooth, sub-ovoid shell. There is a reasonably prominent, anterior-pointing umbo. These specimens are internal casts, the shell material having been dissolved. *Schizodus* grew to about 50mm (2in) in width and is found in rocks of Carboniferous and Permian age. During the Carboniferous period this bivalve lived on the slopes of reefs in moderately deep water. It is found fossilized with crinoids, brachiopods, other molluscs such as *Goniatites*, corals and trilobites. In Permian times, *Schizodus* seems to have been one of the few creatures able to survive the high salinity of enclosed lagoons.

△ **Hippopodium**

This marine bivalve has a massive convex shell with large growth lines that are folded slightly near the umbo. The valves are elongated posteriorly. This genus grew to about 80mm (3¹/₈in) in length, and is found in Lower Jurassic strata in Europe and East Africa. It is frequently associated with a wide variety of other fossils in sandstone and mudstone. These fossils include ammonites, belemnites, and other bivalves. The trace fossil burrow *Thalassinoides* and its associated arthropod *Glyphea* also occur in these strata. *Hippopodium* burrowed with its posterior end level with the sea bed.

◁ **Cardinia**

The two valves of this genus are similar, and are ornamented with thick growth lines and ribs. Its umbones point toward the anterior end of the shell. *Cardinia* grew to about 200mm (8in) in length, and it is found in Triassic and Lower Jurassic strata, worldwide. It occurs in Jurassic sandstone and mudstone strata, with fossils such as ammonites, other bivalves, gastropods and belemnites. *Cardinia* also occurs in the fossil-rich ironstones with the ammonite *Asteroceras*, gastropods and other bivalves.

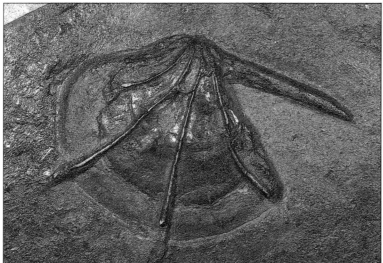

◁ Oxytoma

This bivalve mollusc has a sub-rounded shell. One of the valves is more convex than the other. Beside the umbones are small 'wings'. A spine that extends from this region of the shell is characteristic of the genus. Ribs of different thicknesses ornament the shell. The growth lines are not as pronounced as the ribs. *Oxytoma* grew to about 60mm (2³/₈in) in length. It is found in Triassic, Jurassic and Cretaceous strata, worldwide. In Jurassic sediments it occurs with a variety of other fossils. These include ammonites, other bivalves, belemnites, gastropods and crinoids.

▷ Nuculana

This small bivalve had a sub-triangular shell, with the umbones directed anteriorly. There are concentric growth lines ornamenting the shell. *Nuculana* grew to about 20mm (³/₄in) in length, and occurs in rocks of Triassic to Recent age, worldwide. It burrowed into the sea bed and extended its siphons to the sediment surface. In Jurassic strata – often dark shales that were probably formed in deep, still waters – it is found with ammonites. Also in these rocks are bivalves such as *Oxytoma* and *Inoceramus*. In Cretaceous rocks *Nuculana* occurs with the scaphopod *Dentalium* and a variety of gastropods, as well as ammonites. In Tertiary sediments it occurs with the boring bivalve *Teredo*, fossils of fish teeth, including those of the shark *Odontaspis*, and nautiloids.

◁ Lopha

This oyster is characterized by its exceptionally strong valves, which were able to withstand the turbulent conditions associated with the shallow seas in which it lived. The shell is ornamented with many stout ribs. The two valves shown illustrate both the internal (right) and external (left) features. A large muscle scar and hinge tooth can be seen on the internal surface. The margin between the valves is zig-zag shaped and the valve margins are folded. Like other oysters, *Lopha* was attached to the sea floor during life. It grew to about 120mm (4³/₄in) in length and is found in rocks of Triassic to Cretaceous age, worldwide, including shallow marine strata and shallow reef limestones.

size...
has a...
straight h...
towards the...
are ornamented...
They can be spinos...
have usually broken o...
fossilization. Some specie...
genus were attached to the...
floor by a byssus (a bundle of...
threads), while other species could...
swim freely above the sea bed. It
grew to about 160mm (6¹/₂in) in
diameter, a size of about 100mm
(4in) is more usual. *Chlamys* is
found in rocks of Triassic to Recent
age, worldwide. It occurs in the
same reef limestones as *Lopha*, and
is common in many other shallow-
and moderately deep-water strata.

◁ Exogyra

This oyster has valves of markedly
unequal size. It has developed a
spiral shape, with the umbones
coiled towards the posterior end.
One valve is flat while the other is
convex. The margins of the shell are
rounded and ornamented by radial
ribs. It may also have scales and
spines. The valve margins are
denticulate. The shell is divided by a
deep ridge. During life one valve
was firmly attached to the sea bed.
Exogyra grew to about 200mm
(8in) in length, and occurs in
Cretaceous strata in Europe. In
these rocks it is associated with
fossil sponges including *Siphonia*
and *Hallirrhoa*, as well as other
bivalves, the ammonite
Mantelliceras, echinoids and
brachiopods.

▷ Plagiostoma

Characterized by a reasonably
smooth shell with only faint ribs
and growth lines, this bivalve has
an overall sub-triangular shape. The
posterior is rounded, and there is
an anterior winged extension, near
the umbo. Both valves are convex
and of equal size. There is a single
internal muscle scar. This large
bivalve grew to about 120mm
(4³/₄in) in diameter. It occurs in
Triassic, Jurassic and Cretaceous
rocks, worldwide. Plagiostoma lived
on or just below the sea bed, and
was sometimes attached by a
byssus. In Jurassic sediments it is
found with other bivalves, such as
Gryphaea and *Chlamys*. Ammonites,
belemnites and echinoids are also
found in these rocks. In shallow-
water Jurassic limestones
Plagiostoma is associated with
corals, brachiopods and gastropods.

△ *Chlamys*

This genus has two convex valves in general ... es are strongly ... ard pointing ... mbones. They ... and pronounced 'ears' of different ... s near the umbones. The shell ... rounded margin and a ... inge line, and tapers ... umbones. The valves ... with radiating ribs. ... e but the spines ... ff before ... s of this ... ea

are thick and strikingly ornamented with rows of large tubercles which follow the general shape of the shell. This genus grew to about 100mm (4in) in length, and occurs in Jurassic and Cretaceous rocks,

worldwide. It is commonly found in sediments formed in near-shore marine conditions. In life it is thought to have burrowed shallowly into the sed bed.

▽ *Camptonectes*

This genus has a shell with a rounded margin and a straight hinge line. On each side of the umbones there are prominent 'wings'. The surface of the shell is ornamented with numerous thin growth lines which extend onto the wings. There are also punctations and fine diverging lines on the surface of the valves. This large

bivalve grew up to 200mm (8in) in diameter. It occurs in Jurassic and Cretaceous strata, worldwide. *Camptonectes* was attached by a byssus to the sea bed or other objects. It can be found in sandstones and mudstones with a variety of fossils, including other bivalves, ammonites like *Dactylioceras*, echinoids, brachiopods, and the trace fossil burrow *Thalassinoides*.

◁ *Pinna*

This bivalve has an unusual wedge-shaped (some say ham-shaped) elongated shell. Here it is seen preserved as internal casts, the original shell having been removed, possibly dissolved by acid waters flowing through the sediment. In specimens where the shell is preserved, the umbones are pointed, and the shell surface is ornamented with radiating ribs and marginal undulations. The shell is thin and has a slight ridge running down its long axis. This

genus lived in a burrow, half buried in the sea-floor sediment and attached by a byssus. It grew to a maximum length of about 400mm (16in). *Pinna* occurs in rocks of Lower Carboniferous to Recent age, worldwide. In Carboniferous mudstones, *Pinna* is found with brachiopods, such as *Productus*, goniatites and orthocone cephalopods, gastropods, and bryozoans. In Jurassic clays it occurs with oysters such as *Gryphaea*, burrowing bivalves like *Pholadomya* and *Pleuromya*, and spiriferid brachiopods.

◁ **Pseudomytiloides**
This bivalve has a rounded to sub-triangular shell outline. The shell is thin and the umbones are pointed. The surface of the shell is ornamented with numerous ridges that follow the growth lines. This bivalve grew to about 40mm (1⁵⁄₈in) in length, and is found in strata of Lower Jurassic age in Asia and Europe. It frequently occurs in dark shales preserved in pyrite. In these rocks it occurs with ammonites and other bivalves.

◁ **Laevitrigonia**
This fossil is of the internal cast of the shell of this genus. Many details including the outline of the pallial line and muscle scars are visible on such fossils. In this genus the valves are posteriorly elongated and the umbones are sharp. Recent research has provided details of the soft tissue of *Laevitrigonia*. In some specimens phosphatization has preserved the intestine, gills and muscles. They are very like those of the modern related genus *Neotrigonia*. The specimen shown is a typical size at 50mm (2in) in diameter. It is found in Jurassic rocks in Europe, Asia, East Africa and the Middle East.

▷ **Pseudopecten**
This well-known fossil bivalve has a sub-triangular shell outline. The valves are ornamented by square-sectioned ribs that radiate from the pointed umbones. There are also faint growth lines. On the inside of each valve there is a large muscle scar. This genus belongs to a group which contains some species that are able to swim by flapping their valves together. *Pseudopecten* was probably attached by a byssus to the sea floor. It grew to about 200mm (8in) in width, and is found in Jurassic strata in South America, Europe and the East Indies. This specimen of a Lower Jurassic bedding plane is crowded with disarticulated valves. It is from North Yorkshire, UK.

△ Gryphaea

This common oyster genus has a number of species that are well-known as fossils. It is found in rocks ranging in age from Triassic to Jurassic, worldwide. *Gryphaea* has many specialized features consistent with a sedentary life on the sea bed. Two species are shown. The shell of *Gryphaea arcuata* (above left and above right) has valves that are very dissimilar. One valve is large and curved, while the other is almost flat. The smaller valve fits inside the larger. There are heavy growth lines ornamenting the larger curved valve. The hooked umbo often leans to one side, and there is a radial groove on the posterior side of the larger valve. *G. arcuata* occurs in rocks formed in shallow water. Like many other oysters, when juvenile it was attached to the sea bed by a byssus, but in adulthood simply rested, the heavy hooked valve beneath, on the sediment. *G. arcuata* grew to about 160mm (6½in) in length.

Gryphaea giganteum (above centre) has a much wider and flatter shell than *G. arcuata*. It has a rounded outline with one convex and one concave valve. The heavy, thick shell is ornamented with growth lines. *G. giganteum* reached about 200mm (8in) in diameter.

BIVALVE HABITATS

Bivalve molluscs are adapted to many environments and can survive in sea-water, brackish and fresh-water conditions. Marine genera are most commonly found as fossils. The illustration shows marine bivalves that burrow, swim freely and attach themselves to rocks and other surfaces.

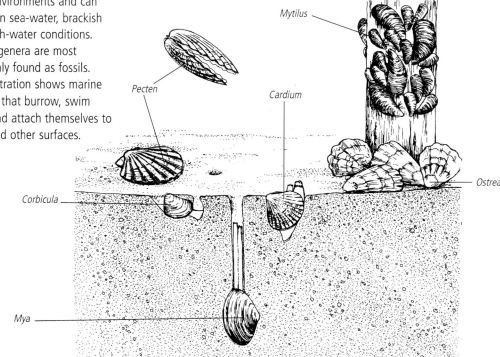

▽ Steinmannia

This genus is characterized by its rounded valve outline and curved growth lines. The short hinge line, on which the umbo is not quite centrally placed, is straight. The fossils shown are the impressions of the valves and their internal sediment filling. It is a common mollusc in Lower Jurassic rocks in Europe, where it is found with other bivalves, cephalopods and belemnites. The pictured specimen is from Yorkshire, UK.

▷ **Modiolus**

This bivalve is closely related to the modern mussel, a well-known bivalve of shallow marine habitats. *Modiolus* has a prominent posterior elongation of its thin shell. The valves are equal in size and the hinge-line is long and straight. The ornamentation consists mainly of concentric growth lines. The small umbones point anteriorly. This bivalve grew to about 100mm (4in) in length, and is found in rocks of Devonian to Recent age, worldwide. It lived attached to the sea bed by a byssus. In Carboniferous strata, deposited in a shallow, possibly highly saline environment, it occurs fossilized with gastropods and worm burrows. In the Triassic period similar conditions existed in lagoonal environments, and here *Modiolus* occurs with the brachiopod *Lingula*. In Jurassic times habitats of shallow sea water

became separated from the main body of the sea where deltas developed. *Modiolus* occurred in these areas with oysters, boring bivalves such as Lithophaga and corals. *Modiolus* is also found in some rocks formed in less

unfavourable conditions, such as Jurassic limestones, where it occurs with a variety of bivalves, gastropods, brachiopods and echinoids.

▽ **Pholadomya**

This bivalve has a shell with a very pronounced posterior elongation, and the valves have a gape between them at this end. The gape, where the valves do not close together, is a typical feature of a burrower, because this allowed the siphons to extend from the shell even when it was confined in a burrow, unable to move the valves apart. The surface of the shell is ornamented with radiating ribs on which there may be small raised tubercles. Concentric growth lines are also present. On the inside surface of the valves there is a deep pallial sinus, another characteristic feature of a burrower. *Pholadomya* grew to about 120mm (4^3/$_4$in) in length, and occurs in rocks of Triassic to Recent age, worldwide. This specimen was found in Lower Jurassic rocks in Gloucestershire, UK.

△ **Inoceramus**

This genus has an ovoid shell outline and elongated umbones that point anteriorly. There are numerous fine growth lines. Some species, like the pictured specimen, have a series of broad ridges running almost at right angles to these. One of the valves is generally more convex than the other. This genus grew to about 120mm (4^3/$_4$in) in length, and is found in a variety of Jurassic and Cretaceous

rocks, worldwide. It lived attached by a byssus to the sea bed or to floating material such as wood. In Jurassic mudstones and shales it is associated with organisms such as the ammonite *Dactylioceras*, belemnites, other bivalves and the bones of marine reptiles. These rocks represent an offshore environment with an oxygen-lacking sea bed. It is also found in limestones that were deposited in conditions more favourable to life,

along with other bivalves, ammonites, echinoids and brachiopods. *Inoceramus* occurs in a variety of rocks of Cretaceous age. It is common in chalk, a fine-grained, powdery limestone. The sea in which this rock formed is thought to have been about 200m (650ft) deep. Here *Inoceramus* occurs with other bivalves, ammonites, sponges, echinoids, and brachiopods.

◁ Spondylus

This bivalve has a sub-rounded, symmetrical shell, with a semicircular margin. The small and pointed umbones may curve slightly in an anterior direction. The surface of the shell is ornamented with fine concentric growth lines and stout ribs. There were, in life, numerous long spines on the shell surface which helped to anchor the shell to the soft sea bed. These have usually broken off in fossils. The specimen in the photograph typically retains only the stumps of some of these delicate spines. On the inside of the shell there is a single muscle scar. This genus grew to about 120mm (4³/₄in) in width, and occurs in rocks of Jurassic to Recent age, worldwide. *Spondylus spinosus* is a common form found in Cretaceous chalk, where it occurs with *Inoceramus*.

▷ Venericardia

This genus has a thick shell with massive hinge teeth. On the inside of each valve are large muscle scars of unequal size. The surface of the sub-triangular shell is ornamented with concentric growth lines and wide, square-sectioned ribs, which have thin grooves between them. *Venericardia* is well suited to life in shallow, possibly turbulent, seas. It lived in a shallow burrow in the sea bed with the posterior part of the shell just at the level of the sediment surface. It is a large bivalve and grew to about 150mm (6in) in diameter. *Venericardia* occurs in Palaeocene to Eocene strata in North America, Africa and Europe. In Eocene sandstones it is found with other bivalves and gastropods.

◁ Hippurites

One valve of this unusual-looking bivalve is tube-like or conical. The other is attached as an operculum (lid). The large valve with its rough, wrinkled and furrowed surface is not unlike a coral in outward appearance. Inside the lower part of this valve there is a series of horizontal divisions. The creature's body occupied only the upper part of this valve. Teeth that project from the larger valve locate in sockets on the lid-like valve, to form a hinge. *Hippurites* lived with the apex of the larger valve attached to the sea bed. The genus often lived in large, coral-like groups, forming reefs in the Tethys ocean of Cretaceous times. Reefs made of these shells are found in many parts of the Mediterranean, where the Tethys was situated. A famous site is near Sorrento in Italy. Some species of the genus *Hippurites* grew to considerable size, reaching over 300mm (12in) in height. Usually specimens are nearer to 120mm (4³/₄in) in height. The genus occurs in Cretaceous rocks in Europe, North Africa and Southeast Asia.

◁ **Eoradiolites**

This genus is similar in certain respects to *Hippurites*. It has a strange shell structure and resembles a coral. The overall shape of the shell is conical and there is a large cone-shaped valve that was attached by its apex to the sea bed during life. A smaller, sub-rounded concave valve acted as an operculum. The larger valve is thick and heavy and ornamented with grooves and wavy ridges. *Eoradiolites* lived in colonies and is often found fossilized in considerable numbers. It grew to about 50mm (2in) in height, and occurs in Cretaceous rocks in North America, Europe and Asia. This specimen is from Iowa, USA.

▽ **Glycimeris**

This common bivalve genus has thick valves and small beaked umbones. The valves are symmetrical and almost circular in outline. The surface ornamentation consists of concentric growth lines and thin radiating ribs. On the internal surfaces of the valves there are large muscles scars joined by a simple pallial line. Two rows of slanting teeth form a hinge mechanism. This genus grew to about 60mm (2³/₈in) in diameter, and occurs in strata of Cretaceous to Recent age, worldwide.

Glycimeris lived just below the sediment surface and is found with many other fossils. It is best known from strata of Tertiary age where it is associated with many bivalves and gastropods. *Glycimeris* is a well-known modern genus living on sandy sea beds in western Europe, from the Mediterranean to Norway.

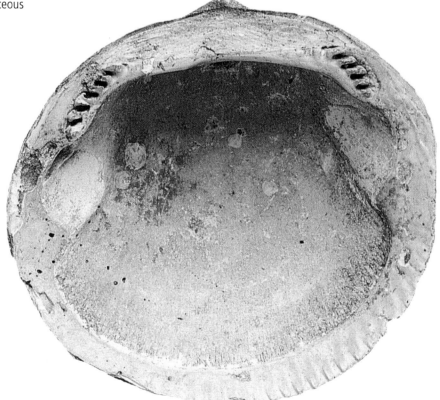

SCAPHOPODS

This class of molluscs is not common in the fossil record. They are characterized by a thin, tapering shell which is generally tube-shaped and open at each end. Modern scaphopods live in the sand of the sea bed with the narrow end of the shell protruding above the sediment. They suck in and expel sea water from this end of the shell. These creatures feed on micro-organisms, such as Foraminifera. The fleshy foot and numerous ciliated arms project from the wider end of the shell. Members of this class also have a head with radula (rasping mouthparts) and feeding tentacles. There are about a thousand living species of scaphopods.

◁ **Dentalium**

The photograph shows three fossil species of this genus of scaphopod. The dark coloured specimen (bottom) is *Dentalium priseum*. The shell has transverse growth lines. It was found in the Carboniferous strata of southern Scotland. The two shells in the centre of the photograph are of *Dentalium sexangulare*. This species has longitudinal ribs and is roughly six-sided. The specimens are from Miocene rocks in Tuscany, Italy. The four thin, tusk-like shells are of *Dentalium striatum* from Eocene rocks in Hampshire, UK.

▷ Pecten

This common bivalve has an almost circular shell outline. The valves are identical in outline, but one is convex or flat, while the other is concave. There are two distinctive 'ears' on either side of the umbones. The valves are ornamented with concentric growth lines and broad radiating ribs. These have numerous smaller lines superimposed on them. *Pecten* is the familiar, often brightly-coloured, scallop shell found in many parts of the world today. Some species can swim by flapping their valves together. It grows to about 80mm (3¹/₈in) in diameter, and occurs in rocks of Eocene to Recent age. The specimen shown is from Miocene strata in Italy.

BORING BIVALVES

Many bivalves burrow into hard materials such as wood. *Teredo*, shown here, uses its tiny shell as a cutting tool to burrow into wood. Some of the wood that it excavates is used as food.

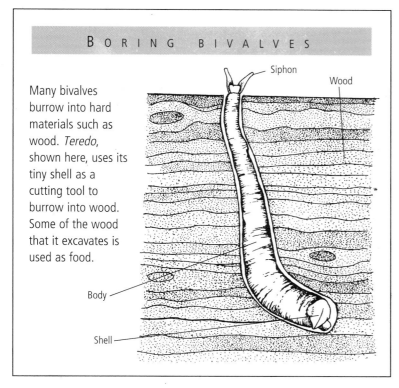

Siphon
Wood
Body
Shell

▽ Teredo

This small bivalve burrows into wood. The specimen shows many individuals in burrows as in life. Frequently only the trace fossil of the burrow is preserved. The soft body of the creature is housed in a tube-shaped tunnel. The burrows are dug by small cup-shaped valves. The tubes shown are about 9mm (³/₈in) in diameter. This strange mollusc is found in rocks of Eocene to Recent age, worldwide. The specimen shown is from Eocene strata of southern England. Because it lived in wood and drifted with logs and other fragments, *Teredo* is found in various sedimentary rocks. In Eocene strata it occurs fossilized with a variety of bivalves and gastropods and with the teeth of sharks such as *Odontaspis*.

9 GASTROPODS

This class of molluscs contains a variety of organisms including some with an external shell and some with no shell. Common modern examples include snails, slugs, limpets and whelks. The class is adapted to many environments. Some commonly fossilized genera are marine, others lived in fresh water. Many gastropods are adapted to living on dry land, and some even climb trees.

Although they are not as well studied as other groups of fossils, these land-dwelling gastropods are the commonest living molluscs. The earliest fossil gastropods are found in rocks of Cambrian age. They are relatively common in Mesozoic strata and abundant in rocks of Tertiary age.

GASTROPOD ANATOMY

Gastropods with shells are more often found as fossils than those without. Gastropod shells are often spirally coiled, though some genera have a cone-shaped shell. The distinguishing feature of gastropods that sets it apart from other molluscs is that its soft body is twisted – a process called

▽ **Straparollus**
This gastropod has a typically coiled shell, which may be reasonably flat or may form a tall spiral. The surface of the shell is smooth, but many thin radiating ribs cross the whorls. There is a slight ridge running along the centre of each whorl. This genus grew to about 50mm (2in) in diameter and is found in rocks ranging in age from

Silurian to Permian. It is well-known in the Carboniferous limestones from which this specimen came. It occurs with a variety of other fossils such as the coral *Caninia*, and various brachiopods, including *Productus*. Molluscs are also found in these shallow-water strata and include bivalves and other gastropods, such as *Bellerophon*.

◁ **Turritella**
This rock surface is composed of masses of shell fragments from this gastropod and other creatures.

◁ **Tentaculites**
This common Palaeozoic fossil is usually considered to be in the group called the pteropods. This contains the modern pelagic and planktonic gastropods. However, some palaeontologists believe that *Tentaculites* lived at least partly buried in the sea-bed sediment. The small shells of this genus are thin and tube- or cone-shaped, with a circular cross-section. They are

ornamented with lateral ridges and some are internally divided by septa. The shells are commonly about 12mm (¹/₂in) in length, and fossils are often found crowded together on bedding planes, as in this example, which also includes brachiopods. *Tentaculites* is found in Silurian and Devonian rocks, especially limestones and sandstones, worldwide.

torsion – early in its life. This causes the mantle cavity to rotate anti-clockwise and the nervous system to adopt a figure-of-eight shape. The shell is composed of calcium carbonate, usually aragonite, which is coated with periostracum. It usually tapers to a point, the apex. There is an aperture at the anterior end, through which the creature's head emerged. This aperture may be modified by a groove, the siphonal canal. In some genera the siphon is a means of drawing water into the gills. A single coil of the shell is called a whorl. The spire consists of the shell minus its last anterior whorl. Inside the shell there is a central axis, the columella. This is often visible in fossils that have been eroded or broken. Gastropods usually have a fleshy foot on which they move. Some genera have an operculum for closing the shell aperture. There are many variations on this general model as can be seen from the specimens shown.

△ Poleumita

The shell of this genus forms a rather flat spiral. The upper surface of the shell is flattened and the lower surface concave. The centre of each whorl is marked with a pronounced ridge. Ornamentation consists of many fine lines, which radiate from the centre (the umbilicus). Small spines are also present. The shell aperture is rather angular. *Poleumita* grew to about 60mm (2³⁄₈in) in diameter, and is common in strata of Silurian age in North America and Europe. The pictured specimen is from limestones in Shropshire, UK. It is found in shallow-water sediments with many other fossils including trilobites such as *Bumastus* and *Dalmanites*, brachiopods, crinoids, corals and fellow gastropod *Tentaculites*.

△ Bellerophon

This gastropod has a bilaterally symmetrical shell that resembles that of a cephalopod, but does not have internal septa or the corresponding suture lines. The shell is rounded and there is a prominent keel around the middle of each whorl. Its outer whorl overlaps and obscures the inner ones. The shell is ornamented with numerous curving ribs, which cross the keel. The aperture is flared and has a deep slit on the front margin. The border of the aperture is narrow and convex. *Bellerophon* grew to about 80mm (3¹⁄₈in) in diameter and has a worldwide distribution in rocks of Silurian to Triassic age. In rocks of Carboniferous age it is found in shallow-water reef-slope limestones along with other gastropods, brachiopods, corals, trilobites and algae.

◁ Mourlonia

This gastropod has a pointed spire-shaped shell that tapers to a narrow apex. The whorls are ornamented with very thin ribs, which radiate from the apex and curve towards the whorl margins. There is a narrow suture between the whorls. This genus grew to about 40mm (1⁵⁄₈in), and occurs in rocks ranging in age from Ordovician to Permian. It crawled on the sea bed and lived in relatively shallow water. It is commonly found in the Permian reef limestones of northeast England, from where the pictured specimens came. In these magnesium-rich limestones, *Mourlonia* occurs with other gastropods, bivalves, brachiopods and reef-binding bryozoans.

◁ **Pseudomelania**

This genus has a long many coiled shell with a pointed apex and deeply set sutures between the whorls. Each whorl has a ridge along it. The specimens shown are preserved as internal moulds, with none of the original shell remaining. They consist of the hardened lime mud that infilled the shells when the creature died. This genus lived by scavenging and sifting through the mud on the sea bed. It grew to about 100mm (4in) in length, and occurs in rocks of Upper Jurassic age in Europe. *Pseudomelania* is found in sandstones and mudstones with other gastropods and various bivalves.

▷ **Bourguetia**

This sea snail has a large, thick-set shell that tapers in typical gastropod fashion to a blunt apex. The outer surface of the shell is often smooth but may be ornamented with growth lines. The whorls are separated by a deep suture. This specimen is from oolitic limestone of Jurassic age, and the numerous small rounded markings on the shell are ooliths, grains from this rock. It grew to about 100mm (4in) in length, and lived in Middle and Upper Jurassic times in the shallow European seas, where it grazed on algae.

▽ **Pleurotomaria**

The whorls of this gastropod's shell coil in a low spiral that gradually widens towards the large and flared aperture. There is a slight groove between the whorls and the overall shape of the shell is slightly asymmetrical. The outside of the shell is ornamented with growth lines, tubercles and spirally arranged bands. *Pleurotomaria* grew to about 120mm (4³/₄in) in height, and is common in rocks of Jurassic and Cretaceous age, worldwide. In Jurassic strata it is associated with ammonites such as *Dactylioceras* and *Hildoceras*, belemnites, bivalves, including *Modiolus* and *Pholadomya*, rhynchonellid brachiopods and corals. *Pleurotomaria* also occurs with oysters and the thin-spired, grazing gastropod *Aptyxiella*. In rocks of Cretaceous age *Pleurotomaria* is found with the ammonites *Turrilites* and *Scaphites*, other gastropods, bivalves, brachiopods, and echinoids.

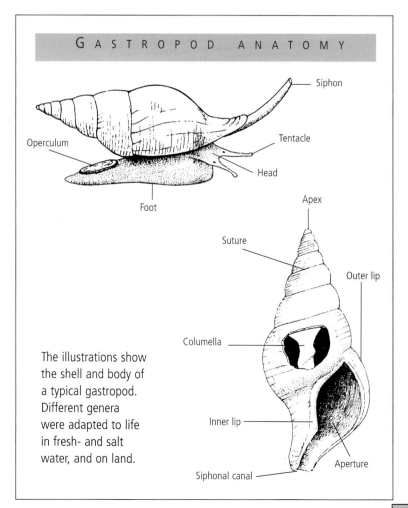

GASTROPOD ANATOMY

Siphon

Tentacle

Operculum

Head

Foot

Apex

Suture

Outer lip

Columella

Inner lip

Aperture

Siphonal canal

The illustrations show the shell and body of a typical gastropod. Different genera were adapted to life in fresh- and salt water, and on land.

◁ Conotomaria

This gastropod genus has a cone-shaped shell in which the indistinct whorls are separated by a medium depth suture. The base of the shell is almost flat. The ornamentation consists of numerous spiral lines and low ridges that encircle the shell. This genus grew to a maximum height of about 150mm (6in), and lived on the sea bed in Middle Jurassic to Palaeocene times, with a worldwide distribution.

▷ Sycostoma

This shapely gastropod has a beautiful shell with a delicate tapering spire. The body whorl is large and inflated. There is a slight shoulder where the whorls meet. The aperture is elongated with a flared margin. The generally smooth shell is ornamented by fine encircling lines and ribs. *Sycostoma* grew to about 70mm (2³⁄₄in) in height, and occurs in strata of Upper Cretaceous to Oligocene age, worldwide.

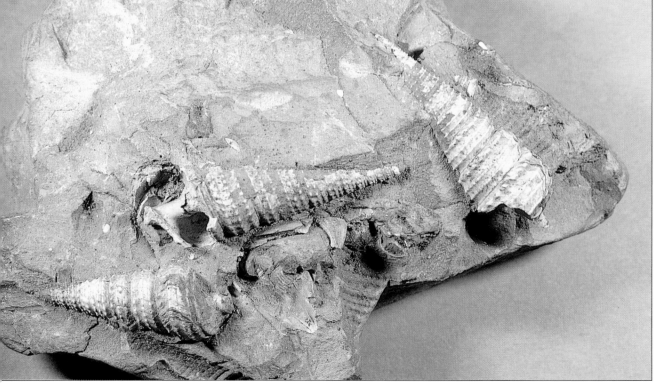

◁ Cerithium

The slender cone-shaped shell of this genus is constructed of numerous small whorls that are separated by slight ridges and ornamented with spines and tubercles. It has a similar overall appearance to *Turritella*, but is distinguished by its greater ornamentation and the obvious canal and flared margin at the anterior end of the pear-shaped aperture. The growth lines follow the margin of the aperture and form an 's'-shape on the final whorl. *Cerithium* grew to about 30mm (1¹⁄₈in) in length and is common in strata ranging from Upper Cretaceous to Recent in age. It is especially well known in Tertiary rocks in Texas, USA, and the Paris Basin, France.

◁ Natica

This gastropod has a thick, smooth shell that is virtually hemispherical. The final whorl is very large compared with the other whorls, which produce a short, flat apex. There are thin sutures between the whorls. Ornamentation consists of very faint curved lines. In life there was an operculum which closed the aperture. This is usually missing in fossils. *Natica* was a carnivorous mollusc that killed its prey (usually small bivalves) by drilling holes in their shells, after having softened them with acid. It grew to about 30mm (1¹⁄₈in) in height, and is found in strata of Cretaceous to Recent in age, worldwide. The specimen in the photograph is from Eocene rocks in the Marne region in France. In rocks of this age, it occurs with a great variety of fossils including other gastropods such as *Turritella*, and bivalves, including *Venericardia*, *Glycimeris* and *Chlamys*. There are also echinoids, sponges and brachiopods in these rocks, which were deposited in shallow marine conditions.

▽ Ancilla

This small gastropod has a tapering shell, which has only faint sutures between the whorls. The final whorl is large in comparison with the others. The aperture is long and tapering and has a broad siphonal notch. There is a variety of ornamentation on the outer surface of the shell, including delicate growth lines and faint longitudinal lines. The shell may have a glossy sheen if preservation is of exceptional quality. This genus grew to a length of about 50mm (2in), and occurs in rocks of Upper Cretaceous to Recent age, worldwide.

△ Ficus

The shell of this gastropod is pear-shaped. The final whorl covers and obscures the other whorls to such a degree that only the pointed apex projects. The large aperture tapers to a narrow base. Ornamentation consists of reticulate criss-cross patterns. *Ficus* grew to a maximum length of about 100mm (4in), and lived in shallow marine conditions in Eocene to Recent times, worldwide. It is found fossilized with a variety of creatures, including other gastropods and bivalves.

▷ Rimella

This small gastropod has an elegantly sculptured shell. It is different from most of the turreted, cornet-shaped shells, in that the anterior section of the final whorl stretches almost to the apex of the shell. The main part of the aperture is in the normal place but the posterior canal extends over the smaller whorls. The aperture has an outer lip around this canal. Delicate curved ribs and spiral markings ornament the shell. *Rimella* grew to about 30mm (1$^{1}/_{8}$in) in length and is found in strata of Cretaceous to Recent age, worldwide.

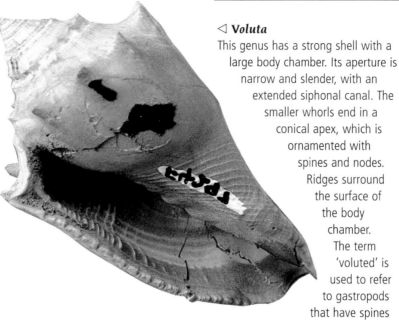

◁ Voluta

This genus has a strong shell with a large body chamber. Its aperture is narrow and slender, with an extended siphonal canal. The smaller whorls end in a conical apex, which is ornamented with spines and nodes. Ridges surround the surface of the body chamber. The term 'voluted' is used to refer to gastropods that have spines and nodes on the shoulders of the whorls, hence the name of this genus. Many genera that were previously assigned to this group have recently been reclassified as *Volutospina* (or *Athleta*). *Voluta* grew to about 120mm (4$^{3}/_{4}$in) in length and is found in strata ranging in age from Eocene to Recent, worldwide. It is a common fossil gastropod in Tertiary strata, especially in rocks formed in shallow marine conditions up to a depth of about 30m (100ft). Other fossils in these rocks include a variety of gastropods, bivalves, the scaphopod *Dentalium*, shark teeth and corals.

▷ Volutospina

This gastropod is sometimes called *Athleta*. It closely resembles *Voluta*, but differs in its ornamentation. *Volutospina* has several weak and one major columellar fold, whereas *Voluta* has four or five folds of similar size. The ornamentation of this genus is of spiral ridges and less pronounced growth lines. Pointed nodes are a typical feature on the shoulders of the whorls. This genus grew to about 120mm (4$^{3}/_{4}$in), in length and is found in rocks of Upper Cretaceous to Recent age. It is particularly common in Eocene strata, worldwide.

▽ Conus

This gastropod has a bi-conical shell, which tapers to a point at each end. The body whorl is large with a long, narrow, parallel-sided aperture. The other whorls form an elongated tapering pyramid, and are ornamented by ridges, growth lines and nodes. The shell surface is rough. *Conus* is often fossilized in great masses, as in the pictured example. It grew to about 120mm (4³/₄in) in length and occurs in strata of Cretaceous to Recent age, worldwide. Today this genus lives in warm seas, such as the Mediterranean. In Eocene times *Conus* lived in similar shallow marine conditions with a great variety of other molluscs, including gastropods and bivalves.

△ Turritella

The shell of this genus is long, narrow and screw-shaped. The whorls overlap only slightly, with deep sutures between them. The body chamber is of similar size to the adjacent whorl and has an almost square aperture. The shell is ornamented with spiral ribs and growth lines. Modern species of this genus, such as *Turritella communis*, burrow into the sea bed with the pointed end of the shell pointing downwards into sediment and the aperture just above the sediment surface. It grows up to 50mm (2in) in length, and occurs in rocks of Cretaceous to Recent age, often in great masses, worldwide.

▽ Cornulina

This gastropod has a highly ornamented shell covered with stout spines and tubercles. The spines are rarely complete in fossils of this genus. The body chamber is large compared with the other whorls. The aperture is flared with a wide lip. The smaller whorls form a pyramid shape that ends in a sharp apex. *Cornulina* grew to about 100mm (4in) in diameter, and is common in rocks of Miocene to Recent age, worldwide.

△ Aptyxiella

This genus is characterized by a thinly tapering shell with a pointed spire. The whorls overlap only slightly, and the body whorl is not much larger than the previous whorl. The shell is usually smooth and lacking in ornamentation. As in the example shown, this genus is frequently found fossilized as internal moulds, with the shell itself missing. *Aptyxiella* grew to about 50mm (2in) in length, and occurs in rocks of Jurassic age, in Europe. It is found in rocks formed in shallow water, where it grazed on algae. Other fossils in these rocks include other gastropods and bivalves, such as oysters. This specimen is from Upper Jurassic strata in southern England.

◁ **Murex**

This is a thick-shelled gastropod with a highly ornamented shell. There is a large body chamber. The rounded aperture has a long siphonal canal and a highly developed lip. The other whorls form a pyramidal spire. The shell ornamentation consists of ribs and spines, which grow in rows. Modern species of *Murex* are carnivorous, and the sexes live separately. This genus grows to about 100mm (4in) in length, and is found in shallow marine strata from Miocene to Recent age, worldwide.

▽ **Globularia**

This gastropod has a rounded shell with a large inflated body chamber and a flared aperture. The smaller whorls produce a flattened cone with a pointed apex. There are many fine ridges running across the shell, and moderately deep sutures divide the whorls. This carnivorous genus preyed on small bivalve molluscs. It grew to about 50mm (2in) in diameter, and occurs in strata of Eocene to Oligocene age, worldwide. It is relatively common in rocks formed in brackish water – for example, in estuaries where fresh and salt water mixed. In these rocks it is associated with oysters, burrowing bivalves, other gastropods and trace fossils of worm burrows.

△ **Hippochrenes**

This elegant marine snail is characterized by a broad, flat extension above the aperture. The feature is ornamented with growth lines and is larger than the rest of the shell. This is pointed at both ends, and has a large body whorl with a sharply pointed siphonal canal. The other whorls are small and narrow. They taper to a sharp apex, which may be partly obscured by the flat shell extension. *Hippochrenes* grew to a length of about 150mm (6in), and occurs in Eocene rocks, in Europe. It lived in shallow seas, probably less than 50m (160ft) deep, where many other creatures also flourished and were fossilized. They include other gastropods and bivalves.

▽ **Galba**

This long and slender freshwater gastropod has a thin shell and a simple aperture. The convex whorls are ornamented with thin growth lines. Along with *Planorbis*, it belongs to the subclass Pulmonata. These gastropods have a lung for breathing air. *Galba* occurs in rocks of Upper Jurassic to Recent age, in Europe, and grows to about 70mm (2³/₄in) in length. It is often found with *Planorbis* and other fresh-water species, mainly bivalves and gastropods.

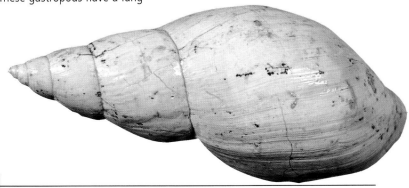

△ *Planorbis*

This gastropod has a shell that is coiled in a flat spiral. On first inspection it resembles that of an ammonite. One side, however, is concave and the other virtually flat, whereas the shell of an ammonite is concave on both sides. The shell surface is smooth with only faint growth lines. There are deep sutures between the whorls. The aperture is oval, or semicircular. *Planorbis* grows to about 30mm (1¹/₈in) in diameter, and is found in strata of Oligocene to Recent age, worldwide. It lives in both still and running fresh water, feeding on algae and other plants. It is a useful indicator of ancient environments of deposition. Some species breathe, using a simple lung and taking in air through their mantle. Other species can stay below water.

▽ *Crucibulum*

This gastropod has a cone-shaped shell that is completely open at the base. It belongs to the family Crepidulidae, the slipper limpets. These 'cup and saucer' shells have a calcareous structure on the inside of the shell that supports and protects the digestive organs. The outside of this shell is ornamented with stout ribs running from the base to the apex. Members of this genus, in common with other slipper limpets, change sex during their lifetime. In modern species of *Crucibulum* the individuals begin as males and turn into females after about three years. With this sex change the creature becomes less active, and adheres to dead shells or rocks. The genus grows to about 50mm (2in) in height, and occurs in rocks of Miocene to Recent age in North America, Europe and the West Indies. The specimen illustrated is from Virginia, USA.

▽ *Turricula*

The slender, tapering shell of this genus finishes in a thin pointed apex. The body whorl is larger than the others and has a long narrow aperture with parallel sides. This whorl is more heavily ornamented than the smaller whorls and has thick, closely set ribs, in addition to the growth lines that cover the entire shell. Each whorl has a row of tubercles around it. *Turricula* grew to about 60mm (2³/₈in) in length, and is found in Eocene rocks, worldwide. Modern members of this genus inhabit warm waters.

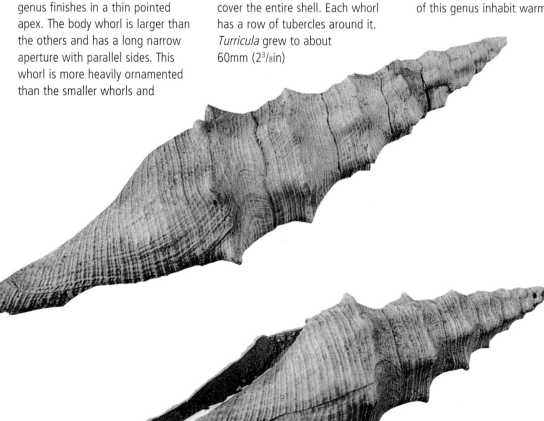

10 CEPHALOPODS

The cephalopods are, and undoubtedly always have been, marine creatures. Their fossils are of great value in the understanding of their evolution, and many of them are ideal zone fossils, allowing accurate correlation and refined relative dating of strata. The cephalopods first appear in the fossil record towards the end of the Cambrian period. There are three main sub-classes of fossil cephalopods: nautiloids, ammonoids and belemnites.

CEPHALOPOD CHARACTERISTICS

Cephalopods differ from the other classes of molluscs in that they have a chambered shell in which gas and liquid can be held. This makes the shell buoyant and therefore allows many of them to float above the sea bed. The most active cephalopods were, and still are, able to swim by jet propulsion. This is achieved by the use of a funnel, known as the hypernome, through which the creature squirts water. The force of the water jet propels the animal forwards. Cephalopods have simple eyes, which provide well-developed sight. The nervous system of members of this class is the most highly developed of the invertebrates.

The body of cephalopods, such as nautiloids and ammonoids, that have an external shell is housed in the first and largest of the shell chambers. This occupies most of the first coil (whorl) of the shell. The body may protrude through the shell aperture. In these cephalopods the smaller chambers are filled with liquid and gas. The modern *Nautilus*, while not very closely related to the ammonoids, has a chambered shell that is the nearest to that of this extinct group. Study of this modern genus therefore provides useful insights into ammonoid lifestyles. *Nautilius pompilius*, a species that lives today in the eastern Indian Ocean and the western Pacific, has buoyancy chambers filled with gas similar to that of the atmosphere, but which has a higher proportion of nitrogen and less of oxygen, and is enriched with argon. This gas fills most of the chambers and is held very close to atmospheric pressure.

◁ **Promicroceras**

This fine specimen contains numerous fossils of the Lower Jurassic ammonite *Promicroceras*. This creature has many of the typical features of the cephalopods, including a coiled shell ornamented with ribs. The rock matrix also contains a number of other molluscs, including bivalves.

The exception is the most recently formed chamber, which contains liquid that is subsequently removed by the creature. These chambers and their contents allow the creature to swim well above the sea bed without having to use up valuable energy in keeping buoyant. The chambered shells of many extinct groups – for example, the ammonoids – are similar in many ways to that of *Nautilus*, although research has proved that the ammonoids are closer relatives of the squids.

Another important structure contained in the coiled shell is the siphuncle. This is a thin tube that runs from the body chamber, through the buoyancy chambers (though not directly linked to them), to the centre of the coiled shell. It probably has an influence on the gas or fluid content of the chambers.

NAUTILOIDS

Members of this sub-class are first found as fossils in strata of late Cambrian age. In rocks of this age they are rare, but during the Ordovician and Silurian periods they become quite numerous as fossils. During the Upper Palaeozoic and Mesozoic eras the number of orders dwindled until by the Cenozoic era only groups closely related to the modern genus *Nautilus* are represented.

Many early nautiloids had straight, orthocone shells that were often of considerable size, reaching over a metre (39in) in length. These animals were probably fierce predators on the Palaeozoic sea bed. The orthocones and the involutely coiled nautiloids such as *Nautilus pompilius*, the modern *Nautilus*, have a number of features that distinguish them from other cephalopods. Where the septa, which divide the shell internally into chambers, meet the outer shell, the sutures are simple and lack great detail. The siphuncle passes through the septa centrally or well away from the ventral surface of the shell (in the ammonoids it is ventrally positioned). Both these features are structural and can be found in fossils. A major feature of the soft tissues, which is unlikely to be found in fossils, is that nautiloids have a great many tentacles, often approaching a hundred, whereas many other cephalopods have very few, usually eight or ten.

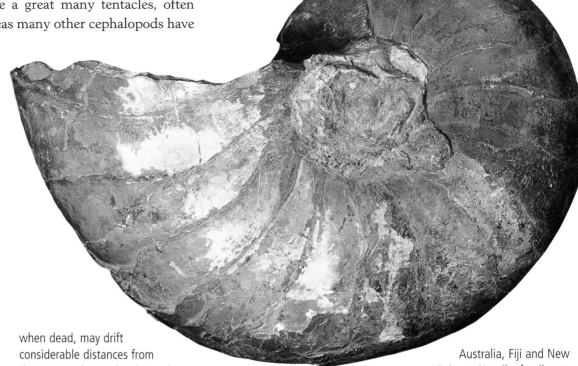

▽▷ **Nautilus**

Two fossils are shown, one of which has been sectioned to show the internal structure. The outer whorls of the shell obscure the inner ones to a great extent. There are simple suture lines that curve forwards slightly near the umbilicus and towards the ventral surface. There is little shell ornament, and apart from fine growth lines the shell is smooth. The body chamber is large and inflated and takes up most of the first whorl. On the sectioned specimen the septa and chambers are clearly visible, as is the central siphuncle. Many of the chambers have been infilled with pale calcite during fossilization. Because of its natural buoyancy, *Nautilus*, even when dead, may drift considerable distances from the region where it lived. Dead shells have been found on the coasts of East Africa, Madagascar, New Zealand, Japan, Myanmar (formerly Burma) and Malaysia – thousands of kilometres from their native waters around the coasts of Australia, Fiji and New Guinea. *Nautilus* fossils are found in rocks of Jurassic to Recent age. It grows to about 150mm (6in) in diameter.

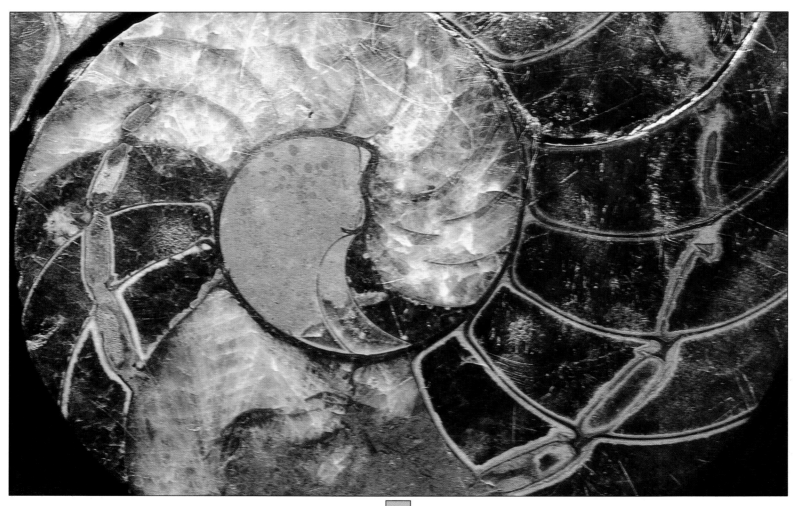

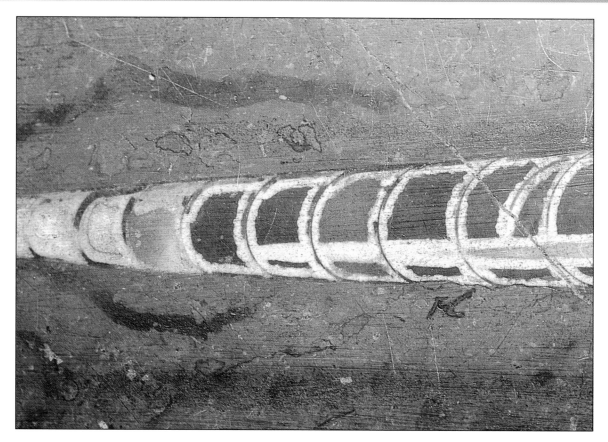

◁ **Orthoceras**

The sectioned specimen of *Orthoceras* shows the septa and the tubular siphuncle. This genus swam or lived near the sea bed with the buoyant shell uppermost and the tentacled body below. However, some shells have been found with shell material inside the chambers, which could have enabled the creature to swim with its shell virtually horizontal. It is thought that the elongated shells of this genus were prone to damage in turbulent conditions. *Orthoceras* grew to great size; specimens several metres long have been found. It occurs in rocks of Lower Ordovician to Triassic age, worldwide. This specimen is from the Silurian strata of Shanghai, China.

▷ **Isorthoceras**

This extinct nautiloid is characterized by a long and slender, slightly tapering shell with a cylindrical cross-section. It is divided into chambers by septa that have simple sutures. The outside of the shell is commonly smooth. This specimen shows a number of fossils aligned in the rock matrix. This arrangement was probably created by the flow of water currents across the sea bed before the shells were buried. Masses of these shells are sometimes so numerous as to form *Orthoceras* limestone. Such deposits occur in Lochkov, Czechoslovakia, and Iowa, USA. This specimen was found in the Ordovician Maquokota formation of Iowa.

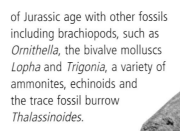

▷ Cenoceras

This nautiloid has a characteristic involute shell, in which the outer whorl covers and obscures the inner whorls. Simple suture lines are visible crossing the shell where some of the outer shell surface is missing. When present, the outer shell has ornamentation consisting of numerous criss-cross lines. As in other nautiloids, the siphuncle is centrally placed. This specimen is 140mm (5$\frac{1}{2}$in) in diameter. Cenoceras is found in rocks of Triassic to Middle Jurassic age, worldwide. It occurs in limestones of Jurassic age with other fossils including brachiopods, such as Ornithella, the bivalve molluscs Lopha and Trigonia, a variety of ammonites, echinoids and the trace fossil burrow Thalassinoides.

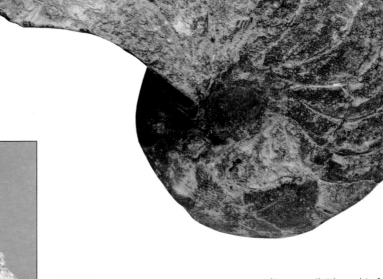

◁ Actinoceras

This orthocone nautiloid has a cylindrical shell divided into chambers. Its large centrally placed siphuncle (not seen in this somewhat broken specimen) has certain identifying features. It is constricted where it passes through the septa and expands as it enters each chamber. The siphuncle is filled with calcified deposits. Similar deposits are found within the chambers. This genus is one of the earliest nautiloids and is found in rocks of Lower Ordovician to Carboniferous age. It is most numerous in the Ordovician and Silurian periods. It has a worldwide distribution. The pictured specimen is 80mm (3$\frac{1}{8}$in) long. Actinoceras occurs in Silurian and Devonian strata with a variety of other fossils including trilobites, a great variety of brachiopods, crinoids, asteroids and bryozoans.

▷ Rhyncholite

This rather strange fossil is part of the jaw mechanism of a nautiloid. The jaws consisted of a strong beak of which this is part. Nautilus, in common with many cephalopods, is an active predator, and its jaws are strong enough to cut through chicken bones. It feeds mainly on invertebrates, such as arthropods, and fish. Fossil rhyncholites have been known for many years. The specimen shown is from the Cretaceous chalk of Norfolk, UK. It is 40mm (1$\frac{5}{8}$in) long.

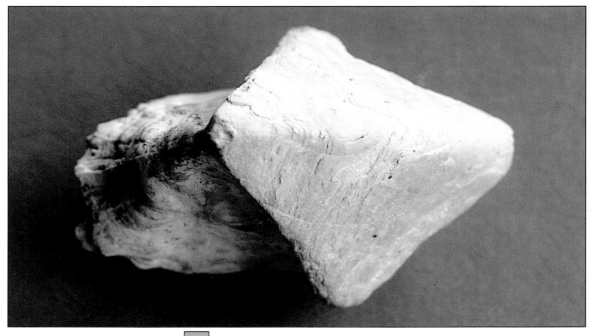

◁ Dawsonoceras

This incomplete shell of an orthocone nautiloid genus can be identified by its stout structure, cylindrical shape, and circular cross-section. The shell tapers only slightly and is ornamented with strong evenly spaced ribs. Fine wavy lines can be seen between the ribs. The genus has a typical centrally placed siphuncle. There are calcareous deposits within the siphuncle and the chambers. In complete specimens the shell at the slightly wider end is devoid of ribbing. This genus grew to a maximum of 750mm (30in) in length. The pictured specimen is 80mm (3¹/₈in) long. *Dawsonoceras* occurs in strata of Silurian age in North America, Europe, Australia and Asia. It is found in shallow-water marine limestones with many other fossils including the trilobite *Bumastus*, brachiopods, corals and gastropods.

▷ Gomphoceras

This nautiloid has an unusual egg-shaped shell. One half of the shell is ornamented with broad ribs, and the rest is smooth. The more sharply pointed end has a curved ridge. The aperture has a slit toward the ventral surface and there is also a small ovoid opening which may be the hole through which the funnel extended. *Gomphoceras* belongs to a group called the Oncocerida, many of which have a large body chamber with a small aperture. They probably lived with the body chamber lowermost. *Gomphoceras* grew to about 80mm (3¹/₈in) in length, and is found in Silurian rocks in Europe. It occurs in shales and limestones with other fossils including the trilobite *Dalmanites*, bivalve molluscs, brachiopods and graptolites.

N A U T I L U S   S T R U C T U R E

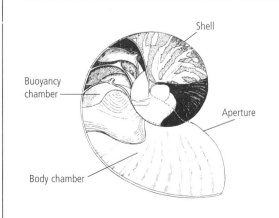

Shell
Buoyancy chamber
Aperture
Body chamber

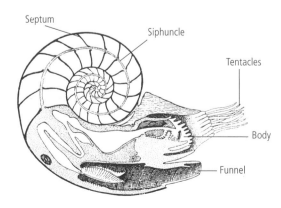

Septum
Siphuncle
Tentacles
Body
Funnel

The structure of the modern *Nautilus* is thought to be similar to that of the extinct ammonoids. The drawings show the main internal (left) and external (far left) features of the *Nautilus*.

AMMONOIDS

This group of cephalopod molluscs first appears in the fossil record in rocks of Devonian age. They developed into an amazing variety of creatures during the Upper Palaeozoic and Mesozoic eras, dying out towards the end of the Cretaceous period. The external ammonoid shell is similar to that of the coiled nautiloids. It is coiled planospirally, and the central umbilicus is depressed from both sides. Shells may be coiled, flat and compressed, or inflated and bulbous; some genera uncoiled, developing a 'rams horn' shape, while others had a gastropod-type shell. Ammonoid shells may be ornamented by a variety of ribs, tubercles and spines. Some had large shells, the biggest being a specimen of *Parapuzosia* from Upper Cretaceous strata of Munster, Germany. This, if complete, would have been 3.5 metres (11ft 4in) in diameter. Such an organism when alive could have weighed 1.5 tonnes. Typical ammonoids, however, are only a few centimetres across. The smallest mature shell on record is only about 3mm (⅛in) in diameter.

The shell is divided internally into many chambers. The largest of these opens at the aperture and extends for approximately the first whorl of the shell. This is the body chamber. Behind this are the buoyancy chambers, which contained a mixture of gases not unlike that of the atmosphere but containing more argon, and fluids. The chambers are partitioned by septa which, where they join the inner surface of the shell whorls, form complex sutures. These sutures help to distinguish ammonoids from nautiloids. In most ammonoids the siphuncle is ventrally placed.

The ammonoid body is known only by analogy with modern cephalopods and from very rare internal fossils, muscle scars and trace fossils. It is believed that ammonoids had a squid-like body with eight tentacles, impressions of which have been found. There was also an ink sac as in the modern coleoids (squids, cuttles and octopods), which presumably had a defensive function. Ammonoid jaws are well documented and are common fossils in the Mesozoic era. These aptychi and anaptychi may occasionally be found in the shell aperture. Originally they were thought to be opercula (doors on the aperture), but their function as a jaw mechanism is now accepted.

THE AMMONOID WAY OF LIFE

Ammonoids were able to move by jet propulsion, using a hypernome (funnel) in a similar manner to the modern *Nautilus*. Their movements were probably quite slow, and many may have grazed on algae on the sea bed, while others may have been benthonic carnivores or scavengers. Shells have been found showing the damage caused by predation. Marine reptiles and fish were probably their greatest enemies.

AMMONOIDS AND TIME

Because of their very rapid evolution and radiation into a great variety of genera and species, ammonoids are of outstanding value as zone fossils. A time zone is the smallest easily managed part of geological time and is recognized by the occurrence of a certain fossil. If that fossil species lived for only a short time, then the rocks deposited when it was alive, and now containing it as a fossil, represent only a small part of

time. Stratigraphy is therefore more precise if the zones are short. The average zone, based on ammonite species, in the Jurassic period is around 800,000 years. They are geographically widespread because they were free moving creatures and even after death their buoyant shells could drift great distances on ocean currents. This allows correlation of strata between distant regions. There are three broad groups of ammonoids each of which lived at a different time. They are easily recognized by their charateristic suture lines. The goniatites lived during the Devonian and Carboniferous periods. In the Permian and Triassic the ceratites were dominant, and the ammonites are the Jurassic and Cretaceous representatives of the class.

▷ Clymenia

The shell of this early ammonoid is smooth and ornamented only with faint ribs radiating from the umbilicus. It has evolute coiling, in which all the whorls can be seen, and the whorl section is rounded. The suture lines are simple. This genus of ammonoids is the only one with a dorsal siphuncle, which can be seen at the top of the first whorl. The genus grew to about 80mm (3¹/₈in) in diameter and occurs in Upper Devonian strata in Europe, Asia and North Africa. The sub-order *Clymeniida* become extinct late in the Devonian period, and thus helps geologists to determine the boundary between strata of the Devonian and Carboniferous periods.

▽ Sudeticeras

This genus of the goniatite group has an involute shell. The overall shape of the shell is globose, and it lacks ornamentation, apart from a series of very fine lines that radiate from the umbilicus. It is a small genus, the specimen shown being only 40mm (1⁵/₈in) in diameter. *Sudeticeras* is found in strata of Carboniferous age in North America, Europe, North Africa and Asia. It was an active swimmer and is found in offshore strata. These include mudstones and shales. In these rocks *Sudeticeras* fossils are associated with those of orthocone nautiloids, bivalves, brachiopods, crinoids and bryozoans.

△ Goniatites

This ammonoid has an involute shell, lacking in surface ornamentation. The unsectioned specimen shows the obscuring of the inner whorls by the large outer whorl. The characteristic suture lines have rounded saddles and pointed lobes. The buoyancy chambers can be seen in the sectioned specimen. This is known to be incomplete because the body chamber is not present. This genus grew to about 50mm (2in) in diameter and occurs in rocks of Carboniferous age in North America, Europe, North Africa and Asia. *Goniatites* was a free-swimming ammonoid, and is found in a variety of strata. It is particularly common in the reef limestones that accumulated on the Lower Carboniferous continental shelves. In this environment many other fossils were formed including other ammonoids, bivalves, gastropods, brachiopods, crinoids and reef-binding bryozoans, like *Fenestella*.

AMMONOID SHELLS

External view

- Umbilicus
- Rib

Cross-section

- Septum
- Buoyancy chamber
- Protoconch
- Aperture
- Body chamber
- Siphuncle

Types of suture lines

- Goniatite
- Ceratite
- Ammonite

The septa, the walls that divide the ammonoid shell into chambers, are joined to the internal surface of the shell by a system of 'fan-vaulting'. The join appears on the inner surface of the whorl as a line known as the suture line or septal suture. These lines can form simple or convoluted shapes according to the particular ammonoid group. Where the lines consist of complex curves, the curves that face towards the shell aperture are called 'saddles'. The backwards facing curves are known as 'lobes'. Suture lines cannot been seen unless the outermost shell surface is missing.

The presence of suture lines on the outer whorl of a specimen indicates that the shell is incomplete. This is because much or all of the final whorl of a complete specimen is normally taken up by the body chamber which is undivided and therefore without sutures. Suture lines can also indicate the maturity of an ammonoid, as they tend to crowd together near the body chamber in adults.

Suture lines have always been thought to be a valuable clue for identifying ammonoids. Certainly there are considerable differences between the suture lines of species and larger groups. The ammonoids have much more complex arrangements of septa, and therefore suture lines, than the similar-shaped *Nautilus*. A variety of theories has been postulated over the years attempting to explain this.

It has been suggested that the presence of complex sutures and their crowding in maturity add to the weight of the shell and so give greater control over buoyancy. In addition, such structures may give the shell greater strength and thereby prevent collapse due to excessive water pressure. This may be important, because the ammonoid shell is relatively thin, especially when compared with that of *Nautilus*. Many ammonoids do not have a rounded whorl section, which provides a strong structure, and so need internal support.

△ *Gastrioceras*

This goniatite ammonoid has an involute shell, with an umbilicus that is somewhat wider than in many other genera. A characteristic feature is a series of nodes around the umbilical margin. These extend into faint ribs across the dorsal part of the outer whorl. The umbilical margin is very steep. The body chamber is long, occupying more than a whorl. *Gastrioceras* grew to about 100mm (4in) in diameter, and is found in strata of Upper Carboniferous age in North America, Europe, North Africa and Asia. It commonly occurs in coal-bearing rock. Various species of *Gastrioceras* are used as zone fossils.

▽ *Prolecanites*

This genus of goniatite ammonoids has a shell in which most of the whorls are visible. Its umbilicus is open and the shell has a rounded ventral surface. The whorls are narrow with parallel sides. Suture lines are clearly visible on this specimen, because the outer shell is missing. The lobes, which face backwards, are pointed and the saddles, which face the aperture, are rounded. We know that this specimen is incomplete because the sutures continue to the end of the shell and the body chamber is therefore absent. This genus grew to about 200mm (8in) in diameter, and occurs in rocks of Lower Carboniferous age.

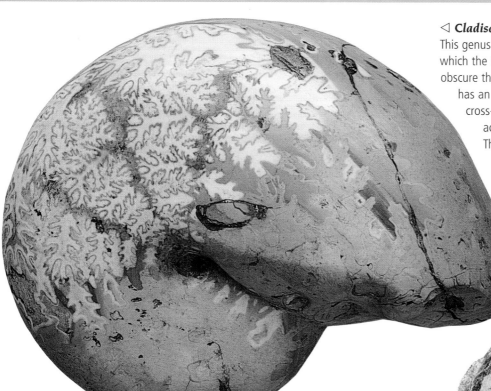

◁ Cladiscites

This genus has an involute shell in which the inner whorls totally obscure the large outer whorl. This has an oval to rectangular cross-section and widens across the ventral surface. The umbilicus is narrow. This specimen lacks its outer shell and the suture lines are clearly visible. These consist of complex lobes and more simple forward-pointing saddles. When present, the outer surface of the shell has unusual ornamentation consisting of fine, concentric ridges, which sweep around the whorls. This genus is relatively large and grew to about 200mm (8in) in diameter. It occurs in marine rocks of Triassic age in Europe (excluding the UK), Alaska and the Himalayas. The specimen shown is from Austria.

▷ Joannites

This ammonoid has a rounded, almost globular shell. The involution of the whorls is so extreme that the umbilicus is virtually obscured, being merely a small central hollow. The outer surface of the shell has little ornamentation apart from thin, slightly curving ribs. This genus has more complex suture lines than many ammonoids of the same period. The specimen illustrated is typical at 60mm (2³/₈in) in diameter. It occurs in marine strata of Triassic age in North America, continental Europe, and the Himalayas. This specimen is from Austria.

◁ Monophyllites

The shell of this genus is involute, although the inner whorls are not totally obscured. The thin shell is ornamented externally with fine, closely packed ribs. The whorls are rounded in cross-section, and there are visible sutures. It has been argued that these creatures lived at greater depths than many other ammonoids. *Monophyllites* is one of the earliest phyloceratids, a group that lived from the Triassic to the Cretaceous periods. Members of this genus grew to about 100mm (4in) in diameter, and are found in Triassic rocks in North America, continental Europe and Asia.

▽ **Echioceras**

This ammonite has an evolute shell in which all the whorls are easily seen. Numerous evenly spaced ribs radiate from the umbilicus. These cross the venter, but are interrupted by a low keel. The whorl cross-section is rounded. This genus grew to about 100mm (4in) in diameter, and occurs in Lower Jurassic strata, worldwide. The pictured species, *Echioceras raricostatum*, is used as a zone fossil. This genus is fossilized in a variety of sedimentary rocks, especially shales and limestones, and is found with a wide variety of other fossils, including other ammonites, bivalves, belemnites, crinoids, fish and vertebrates.

△▽ **Hildoceras**

Both pictured specimens are *Hildoceras bifrons* from the Lower Jurassic strata of North Yorkshire, UK. Specimens of this genus are common in the dark shale cliffs near St. Hilda's Abbey, Whitby, North Yorkshire, hence the name. This species is a zone fossil for part of the Lower Jurassic period. The inner whorl of the shell is partly visible. The ribs, which ornament the outer surface of the shell, are characteristically sickle-shaped.

There is a keel on the ventral surface, which has furrows on either side. The genus grew to a maximum of about 120mm (4³/₄n) in diameter. It occurs in Lower Jurassic strata in Europe, Asia Minor and Japan. It is a common fossil in a variety of sedimentary rocks, and is especially well known in dark shales, where it occurs with fossils of other ammonites, such as *Dactylioceras* and *Harpoceras*, and bivalve molluscs, including *Gryphaea* and *Oxytoma*.

△ **Oxynoticeras**

The typical 'oxyconic' shell structure of this genus consists of a flattened involute shell in which the inner whorls are almost totally obscured by the outer whorl. The shell surface is ornamented with closely-packed ribs that radiate from the small umbilicus. These ribs cross the sharp ventral surface, and curve forwards slightly. *Oxynoticeras* grew to about 35mm (1³/₈in) in diameter, and is found in Lower Jurassic rocks in Europe, North Africa, South America, Japan and Indonesia. This species, *Oxynoticeras oxynotum*, is a zone fossil.

△ *Promicroceras*

This small ammonite has an evolute shell with all the whorls clearly visible. The whorls have a rounded cross-section. Thick ribs that radiate from the wide umbilicus ornament the surface. These curve slightly as they reach the ventral surface, and are flattened where they cross it. This genus grew to about 30mm (1¹⁄₈in) in diameter, and occurs in rocks of Lower Jurassic age in Europe. This specimen consists of a large number of fossils packed closely together with very little rock matrix. Some fossils retain their outer shell, while in others it has broken off to reveal the suture lines. This specimen is a small part of the famous Marston Marble from Somerset, UK.

▷ *Microderoceras*

An ammonite with evolute coiling and an open umbilicus, *Microderoceras* is ornamented with faint ribs that radiate from the centre of the shell. The ribs have pairs of sharp nodes. These are evenly spaced – one near the ventral surface and the other near the dorsal margin of each whorl. Often these are worn down in fossils. This genus grew to a maximum of about 150mm (6in) in diameter, but most specimens are smaller. *Microderoceras* occurs in strata of Lower Jurassic age in Europe.

◁△ *Dactylioceras*

This common ammonite has a shell with serpenticone (snake-like) evolute coils. The whorls are rounded in cross-section, except for a slight saddle on the inner curve where one whorl rests on the next. The ribs that ornament the outer surface divide in two (bifurcate) where they cross the ventral surface. In some species there are rows of tubercles arranged on the inner whorls. *Dactylioceras* grew to about 100mm (4in) in diameter, and is found in strata of Lower Jurassic age, worldwide. The specimen (top left) has had a snake's head carved on it. This is likely to be a reference to a legend that St Hilda, who founded an abbey in Whitby, North Yorkshire, UK, where these fossils are very common, had turned the local snakes to stone. In some areas, especially near Holzmaden in Germany, *Dactylioceras* occurs in great masses.

◁ *Eparietites*

This genus of ammonites grew to considerable size, often reaching over 500mm (20in) in diameter. It has an involute shell, in which only part of each inner whorl is visible. The umbilical margin is steep, and the whorl cross-section narrow, the sides converging toward the sharp-keeled venter. The body chamber of this worn specimen can be distinguished from the buoyancy chambers by its different colouring. The body chamber is greyish and filled with sediment after the death of the animal. The buoyancy chambers are infilled with calcite and other minerals, and are coloured black and white. Fossils of this genus are found in Lower Jurassic rocks in Europe. The specimen is from the Frodingham Ironstone of Lincolnshire, UK.

◁ **Harpoceras**
This genus has a rather flat, involute shell. It is characterized by a large outer whorl and a sharp ventral keel. The sickle-shaped ribs radiate from the umblicus. They do not cross the venter. The whorl cross-section is narrow, and the umbilical margin is steep. This ammonite grew to about 200mm (8in) in diameter, and occurs in strata of Lower Jurassic age, worldwide. The pictured specimen is *Harpoceras falciferum*, which is a zone fossil. It often occurs in dark shales with other ammonites, bivalve molluscs, belemnites and the bones of marine reptiles.

▷ **Arnioceras**
All the whorls of this evolute ammonite shell are clearly visible. The ventral surface of the shell has a sharp keel with a narrow groove on either side. There are ribs on the whorls that radiate from the centre of the shell. This specimen is of considerable interest because part of the jaw mechanism, the anaptychus, is preserved near the shell aperture: the structure is strikingly similar to the jaws of modern squids. *Arnioceras* grew to about 50mm (2in) in diameter, and occurs in Lower Jurassic rocks, worldwide.

▷ **Pleuroceras**
Two specimens of this evolute ammonite are shown. In cross-section the whorls are almost rectangular. The shell is ornamented with thick, well-spaced ribs. Tubercles and spines occur on the ribs, usually near the ventral surface. These are often worn or broken off in fossils. Along the ventral surface there is a keel with a corded structure. The ribs do not cross the venter. Both specimens have complex suture lines. The paler specimen, which was found in limestone, has suture lines to the end of the last whorl, indicating that the body chamber is missing. In the dark specimen suture lines are absent from much of the final whorl, indicating that at least some of the body chamber is present. In addition, the last two or three sutures are crowded closely together, suggesting that this is a mature shell. This genus grew to about 100mm (4in) in diameter and occurs in strata of Lower Jurassic age, in Europe and North Africa. The species *Pleuroceras spinatum* is a zone fossil.

SEXUAL DIMORPHISM IN AMMONITES

For many years it has been suggested that in ammonites differences in shell size may be an indicator of sexual dimorphism – the existence of different male and female forms within the same species. The smaller shell of a given species is known as the microconch (m) and the larger shell is the macroconch (M). The macroconch may be up to five times larger than the microconch. The sexes of many modern cephalopods differ in size. The female *Argonauta argo*, for example, is up to twenty times larger than the male. It is not easy to distinguish between male and female in fossils because of the lack of soft parts. Many palaeontologists regard the larger shells as female and the smaller ones as male because the females may require larger shells to house their ovaries. Moreover, the lappet, an extension from the aperture in the microconch of some ammonite genera – for example, *Kosmoceras* – may have had a male reproductive function similar to that of the spadix of the modern *Nautilus*.

IDENTIFYING MALE AND FEMALE

A number of criteria need to be met before it is possible to say that two ammonites are, in fact, the male and female of the same species. The shells must be of precisely the same geological age and be proved to have a close genetic relationship. New features developed in the genus must arise at the same time as the evolution of the group progresses. Their shell structure must be very similar – often the inner whorls of the macroconch are identical to the entire microconch. However, the detailed pattern of coiling, rib ornamentation and other features may differ, and in some cases the macroconch may be more involute than the microconch. Smaller shells may also possess particular structures, such as lappets. For a valid comparison to be made, the shells must be complete and mature. The broken shell of a macroconch could be mistaken for that of a microconch in the absence of other defining features. Unless the relative maturity of

a specimen can be judged, there is also a risk of confusion – for example, a juvenile macroconch could be wrongly identified as a mature microconch. Mature shells often show a crowding of the suture lines near the body chamber and the final whorl may uncoil slightly. In addition, as an individual ages, ornamentation of the final part of the body chamber, close to the aperture, changes: the ribs may degenerate, and a flaring of the aperture may occur. Microconches (supposed males) develop extensions of the shell such as the lappets, and rostra. A rostrum is a forward projection of the ventral surface of the aperture as seen in *Aegoceras*.

SEXUAL INEQUALITY

In some collections the 'male' microconches are far outnumbered by the larger 'female' shells. This does not necessarily mean that the males had large harems! The study of modern cephalopods shows that sexual segregation occurs, and that in the populations of some genera the females outnumber the males significantly. In other groups the opposite is true. Also sexual groups seem to migrate together, as do groups of immature individuals. Such behaviour may influence the fossil record. A problem with the theory of sexual dimorphism in ammonites is that of the naming of the two shell types. As can be seen by the four pairs on page 139, the micro- and macroconches have different generic names. This is simply a result of their having been first named and described many years ago before they were recognized as dimorphic pairs. According to the rules of biological nomenclature the first published name is the one which is used thereafter. Many of the more recently identified dimorphic pairs do, however, have the same generic names, for example, the species of *Kosmoceras*.

◁ **Brasilia (M)** *and* **Ludwigella (m)**
The photograph shows the two fossils in the same bed of oolitic limestone. Their shells are very similar, having the same type of involute coiling in which the outer body whorl obscures most of the inner whorls. Numerous closely spaced, sickle-shaped ribs ornament the shell surface. These curve forwards just before they cross the sharp-keeled venter. When complete (this specimen is broken), the microconch has a lappet. The aperture of the macroconch is plain. *Brasilia* grew to about 200mm (8in) in diameter, and *Ludwigella* reached about a third of this size. These ammonites are found in rocks of Middle Jurassic age in Europe, Iran and North Africa. This specimen is from Dorset, UK.

▷ **Liparoceras (M) and Aegoceras (m)**

This is a sexually dimorphic pair from Lower Jurassic strata of Gloucestershire, UK. *Liparoceras*, the macroconch, has a stout involute shell with thick, well-spaced ribs that bifurcate as they cross the venter. The ribs have pairs of sharp nodes near the umbilical margin and at the point where the ribs bifurcate. This shell grew to about 100mm (4in) in diameter. *Aegoceras*, the microconch, closely resembles the inner whorls of *Liparoceras*. It has evolute coiling and strong ribs cross the shell. These ribs have weak tubercles. *Aegoceras* grew to 60mm (2³/₈in) in diameter. Careful study of these ammonites has shown an evolutionary sequence. Both macro- and microconch show similar development. Both forms occur in strata of Lower Jurassic age. The macroconch has been found in Europe, North Africa and Indonesia, while the microconch has been found only in Europe.

◁ **Procerites (M) and Siemiradzkia (m)**

There is an extreme size difference between the two ammonites in this dimorphic pair. *Procerites*, the macroconch, has a sub-evolute to involute shell with broad, flattened whorls. In less worn specimens than the pictured example, the shell surface is ornamented with radiating ribs that bifurcate as they cross the venter. It grew to about 300mm (12in) in diameter. *Siemiradzkia*, the microconch, is very similar to the innermost whorls of the macroconch and has the same style of bifurcating ribs. This ammonite grew to only 40mm (1⁵/₈in) in diameter. Both ammonites are from strata of Middle Jurassic age, worldwide. These specimens were found at Cape Mondego in Spain.

▷ **Ludwigia (M) and Ludwigina (m)**

In this example, the macroconch, *Ludwigia*, has sub-evolute coiling, with the inner whorls moderately obscured by the body whorl. The umbilical margin is steep and the shell surface is ornamented with sickle-shaped ribs. These bifurcate before they reach the sharp-keeled ventral surface. This ammonite grew to about 120mm (4³/₄in) in diameter. This species, *Ludwigia murchisona*, is a zone fossil. *Ludwigina*, the microconch, has similar coiling and shell ornamentation. The suture lines end just after the start of the final whorl, indicating the completeness of the specimen. This genus grew to about 40mm (1⁵/₈in) in diameter. Both specimens are from Middle Jurassic strata of the Isle of Skye, Scotland.

◁△ **Lytoceras**

This ammonite has loosely coiled, evolute whorls. The cross-section is rounded, and the size of the shell increases rapidly towards the aperture. Ornamentation consists of fine ribs and radiating lines. Near the aperture there may also be stouter ribs. The suture lines are very complex and may be moss-like. One of the two specimens shown is broken; only part of the outer whorl is present. This ammonite belongs to the lytoceratid group, which is found throughout the Jurassic and Cretaceous periods. *Lytoceras* grew to about 150mm (6in) in diameter. It occurs in Jurassic strata, worldwide.

△▷ **Psiloceras**

Psiloceras planorbis is the oldest zone fossil of the Jurassic period. Usually it is crushed flat on shale bedding planes, as in the specimen (right). Here the original shell material is preserved, and the fine wavy ribs can be seen, especially near the aperture. The other specimen (above) is preserved in three dimensions – a rarer occurrence. The shells seen in this specimen have sub-evolute coiling and the whorls have a rounded cross-section. The complex suture lines are visible and in many cases the sutureless body chamber can be seen. *Psiloceras* grew to about 70mm (2³⁄₄in) in diameter, and occurs in Lower Jurassic strata in North America, South America, Europe and Indonesia.

◁ Amaltheus

The shell of this genus has a rather flattened involute to sub-evolute construction. The whorl cross-section is 'oxyconic' (flattened with a sharp ventral surface). There is a corded keel along the venter. The radiating ribs curve forwards slightly near the venter but are interrupted by the keel. Much of the inner whorl detail is obscured by sediment in this specimen. *Amaltheus* grew to about 80mm (3¹/₈in) in diameter. It is used as a zone fossil for part of the Lower Jurassic period. It occurs in North America, North Africa, Europe and Asia, and is found in a variety of sedimentary rocks including shale, sandstones and limestones.

▷ Tragophylloceras

With its highly involute structure, this genus resembles the shell of *Nautilus*. The shell is flattened, and the only ornamentation consists of fine, closely packed ribs which curve slightly between the umbilicus and the venter. One of the pictured specimens shows the suture lines where the shell is partly broken. It grew to about 90mm (3¹/₂in) in diameter, and occurs in strata of Lower Jurassic age. The species *Tragophylloceras ibex* is used as a zone fossil. It is found worldwide.

◁ Asteroceras

Most of the inner whorls of this ammonite shell can be seen. It is ornamented with thick, widely spaced ribs, which curve forwards slightly near the venter. The ribs do not cross the narrow keel and its border furrow. In this beautiful specimen from Dorset, UK, the buoyancy chambers are infilled with pale calcite and the body chamber is filled with sediment. In some cases the body chamber, with sediment infilling, is preserved three-dimensionally, while the buoyancy chambers are crushed because sediment cannot enter them. *Asteroceras* grew to about 100mm (4in) in diameter, and occurs in Lower Jurassic rocks in North America, Europe and Asia. The species *Asteroceras obtusum* is a zone fossil. The genus is commonly found with a variety of fossils including other ammonites, bivalves, crinoids, brachiopods and trace fossil burrows.

△ **Morrisiceras**
This ammonite has a rounded involute shell. The umbilicus consists of a deep circular hollow in the centre of the shell. Thin ribs cross the ventral surface but gradually disappear towards the umbilicus. In incomplete specimens where the inner whorls are visible the ribs bifurcate. This genus grew to about 80mm (3$\frac{1}{8}$in) in diameter. It is found in rocks of Middle Jurassic age in Europe, with a variety of other fossils including bivalve molluscs, gastropods, brachiopods and echinoderms.

▽ **Stephanoceras**
The shell of this ammonite has evolute coiling. Its shell is ornamented with strong ribs. On the flanks the ribs are thick and widely spaced. Half-way to the ventral surface a node develops, from which the ribs bi- or trifurcate (split into two or three). There is no keel on the venter. The umbilicus is quite deeply set, and the whorls have a rounded cross-section. Stephanoceras grew to about 150mm (6in) in diameter. It occurs in Middle Jurassic rocks, worldwide, often with other molluscs and brachiopods. Stephanoceras humphriesianum is a zone fossil.

▽ **Leioceras**
Two specimens of this ammonite are shown. One has been sectioned to show the internal details. The shell (clearly seen in the unsectioned specimen) is flattened and has involute coiling, only the smallest amount of the inner whorls being visible. The complex suture lines are visible in this rather worn example. These reach to the end of the largest whorl, indicating that the specimen is incomplete. In less worn specimens, the surface of the shell is ornamented with thin, closely packed ribs, which curve in a sickle-shape. There is a narrow keel along the ventral surface and this interrupts the ribs. In the sectioned specimen the body chamber and the first five buoyancy chambers are filled with oolitic limestone. This is composed of small grains of calcite composition and larger particles of calcite, which are probably shell fragments. The rest of the buoyancy chambers are filled with crystalline calcite. Leioceras grew to about 100mm (4in) in diameter, and occurs in strata of Middle Jurassic age, in Europe, North Africa and the Middle East. Leioceras opalinum is a zone fossil.

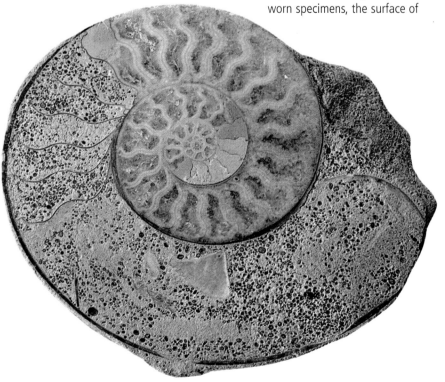

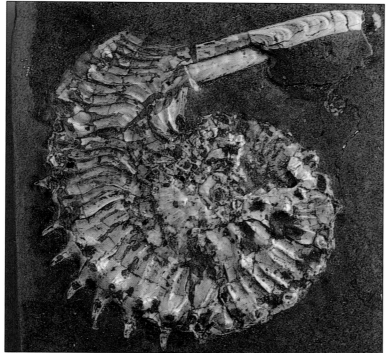

△▷ *Kosmoceras*

Three species of this ammonite genus are illustrated. It has an involute to sub-evolute shell ornamented with various styles of ribs and tubercles. The crushed specimen (above), which is from the Oxford Clay of southern England, is a typical microconch with a complete shell and well-developed lappet. It has strong ribs across its shell. The uncrushed, brownish coloured specimen (right) is from Middle Jurassic strata at Thouars in western France. This specimen has fine, closely packed ribs that cross the ventral surface. The dark specimen (above right) is from the Oxford Clay of southern England, and shows coarse ribbing with equally spaced nodes.

Kosmoceras grew to about 60mm (2³/₈in) in diameter and occurs in Middle Jurassic rocks, worldwide.

◁ *Chondroceras*

This small ammonite has a rounded, almost bulbous shell. The coiling is highly involute, and the shell has a rounded cross-section. The ornamentation consists of numerous closely spaced ribs which divide into two or three before they cross the venter. This ammonite grew to only 40mm (1⁵/₈in) in diameter, and is found in rocks of Middle Jurassic age in North America, Europe, North Africa, Indonesia and New Guinea. It occurs with a variety of fossils including bivalve molluscs, brachiopods and other ammonites.

◁ Witchellia

This genus has highly involute coiling, the umbilicus being hardly visible. The shell is flattened and has a prominent ventral keel. Ornamentation consists of radiating ribs, which owing to wear cannot be clearly seen in this specimen. However, the wearing of the shell has revealed the complex suture lines. The microconch of this genus developed a rostrum, and the lappet curved inwards constricting the aperture. *Witchellia* reaches about 100mm (4in) in diameter, and is found in strata of Middle Jurassic age, in Europe.

▷ Sphaeroceras

This ammonite shell is globose with involute coiling. The inner whorls are totally obscured by the large inflated outer whorl, and the umbilicus is closed. In complete specimens, such as the one shown, the aperture has a flared collar around it. Well-developed ribs that bifurcate before they cross the venter form the chief shell ornamentation. The ribs are often less pronounced when they cross this surface. The whorls have an oval cross-section, and the last whorl may be incompletely coiled. *Sphaeroceras* is a small ammonite that grew to only about 30mm (1 1/8in) in diameter. It occurs in strata of Middle Jurassic age in Europe, North Africa, Iran and Alaska. This specimen is from Bayeux, France.

◁ Parkinsonia

The open-coiled, evolute shell of this common genus is described as serpenticone, or snake-like. Many ammonites have this type of shell. The ornamentation consists of radiating ribs which bifurcate near the venter. There is a slight groove running around the venter, across which the ribs do not pass. This feature helps to distinguish the ammonite from *Dactylioceras*, an ammonite of similar appearance. The whorls of *Parkinsonia* have a compressed cross-section. This genus grew to about 150mm (6in) in diameter, and is found in rocks of Middle Jurassic age in Europe, Asia, North Africa and Iran. *Parkinsonia parkinsoni* is a zone fossil. It often occurs in oolitic limestones with a great variety of other fossils including bivalves, gastropods, brachiopods and echinoids.

▽ Graphoceras

The inner whorls of this ammonite are virtually hidden by the involute coiling and the umbilical shoulder is steep. In common with a number of other genera, *Graphoceras* has sickle-shaped ribs. These bifurcate near the sharp venter. Complex suture lines are visible on the specimen, which is from Dorset, UK. *Graphoceras* grew to about 80mm (3¹/₈in) in diameter, and it occurs in rocks of Middle Jurassic age in Europe, Asia and Africa. *Graphoceras concavum* is a zone fossil.

△ Cardioceras

The shell of this genus has sub-evolute coiling that reveals some of the inner whorls. The radiating ribs bifurcate before they cross the venter and there are shorter ribs between the main ones. All the ribs curve forwards near the venter and there are often tubercles where the ribs bifurcate. The ventral keel is corded. Sexual dimorphism is well known in this genus. The microconch has a rostrum that extends from the ventral part of the aperture, and the macroconch has a smooth body chamber. The macroconch is typically 125mm (5in) in diameter, and the microconch grew to about 60mm (2³/₈in) in diameter. This genus is found in Upper Jurassic rocks, worldwide. *Cardioceras cordatum* is a zone fossil.

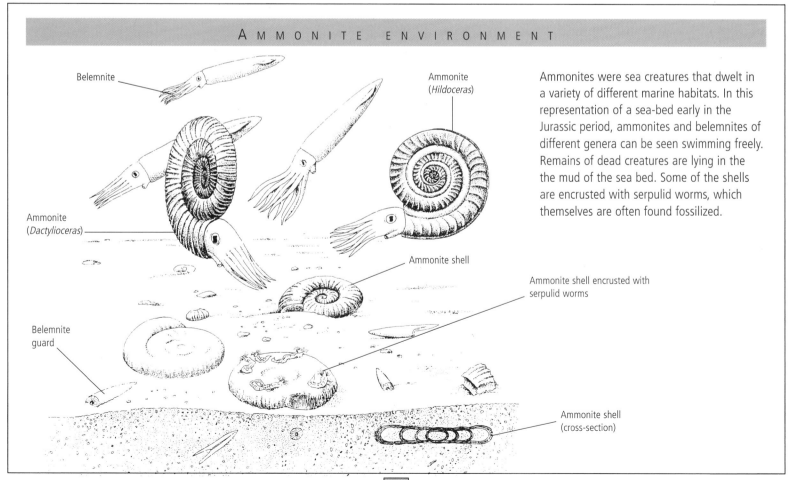

AMMONITE ENVIRONMENT

Belemnite

Ammonite (*Hildoceras*)

Ammonite (*Dactylioceras*)

Ammonite shell

Ammonite shell encrusted with serpulid worms

Belemnite guard

Ammonite shell (cross-section)

Ammonites were sea creatures that dwelt in a variety of different marine habitats. In this representation of a sea-bed early in the Jurassic period, ammonites and belemnites of different genera can be seen swimming freely. Remains of dead creatures are lying in the the mud of the sea bed. Some of the shells are encrusted with serpulid worms, which themselves are often found fossilized.

△ Quenstedtoceras

This genus has sub-evolute coiling of the shell, and is ornamented with strong ribs. The main ribs are sickle-shaped and there are shorter secondary ribs between them. There is no keel on the ventral surface but the secondary ribs produce a chevron pattern there. One of the specimens shown is broken so that the internal buoyancy chambers can be seen. This ammonite exhibits sexual dimorphism. All the shells shown are microconches. When complete these have a rostrum that extends from the ventral part of the aperture. The macroconches have less ornamentation, especially on the body chamber, and their aperture is simple. The microconch grew to about 60mm (2³/₈in) in diameter; the macroconch is about three times this size. The genus occurs in rocks of Middle and Upper Jurassic age, worldwide.

◁ Choffatia

An ammonite with evolute coiling of its whorls, this genus is the macroconch of a dimorphic pair. It is ornamented with radiating ribs that bifurcate across the venter, where they are less pronounced. The aperture is simple and the whorl cross-section rounded. It grew to about 120mm (4³/₄in) in diameter, and occurs in Upper Jurassic rocks in North America (including Alaska), Chile, the Himalayas, Iran, Europe, and North and East Africa.

◁ Pavlovia

The specimen illustrated has been virtually crushed on a shale bedding plane, though some of the original calcareous shell material is still present. Often this genus is preserved as small sections of the whorls, infilled with sediment. The coiling is sub-evolute and the inner whorls are clearly seen. The whorl cross-section is circular. Strong ribs ornament the shell. These bifurcate near the venter, which has no keel. This large genus grew to about 400mm (16in) in diameter, and occurs in Upper Jurassic rocks in Europe, Greenland and Asia. It is found with a variety of other fossils including other ammonites, bivalves and the brachiopod *Lingula*. The species *Pavlovia rotunda* and *P. pallasioides* are zone fossils.

▷ Amoeboceras

This genus has involute coiling. On unworn shells the main ribs are strong and well spaced. Shorter secondary ribs appear near the venter. The ribs do not cross the venter and are interrupted by a corded keel. This specimen is of interest because it shows a feature associated with maturity in ammonites. The final few suture lines, visible on the shell where it has become worn, crowd together just before they end at the body chamber. The presence of the un-sutured body chamber confirms the completeness of the specimen. *Amoeboceras* grew to about 80mm (3¹/₈in) in diameter, and occurs in Upper Jurassic rocks in Europe.

◁ Titanites

One of the largest of the ammonites, this genus has evolute coiling with the inner whorls easily seen. The ribs are well spaced on the inner whorls but they crowd together on the outer whorl. These ribs bifurcate across the venter where they become less pronounced. The specimen illustrated has the typical dark colouring near the aperture which is found on many examples of *Titanites*. This genus grew to over a metre (39in) in diameter. It occurs in strata of Upper Jurassic age in northern Europe, Greenland, Canada and Asia. *Titanites* is found with other molluscs, including a variety of bivalves. The crustacean *Callianassa* also occurs with these fossils. The specimen illustrated is from Dorset, UK. *Titanites giganteus* is a zone fossil.

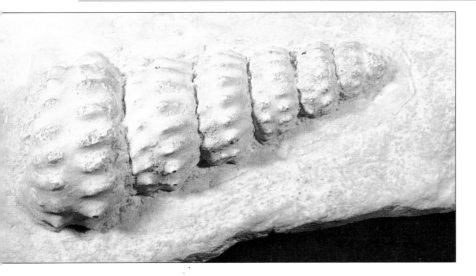

△ Turrilites

Some ammonites developed bizarre shell shapes, especially toward the end of their evolution. This shell is, on first observation, not unlike that of a gastropod, with a spiral (helicoid) structure, but is identified as that of an ammonite by its suture lines and chambered internal structure. The whorls rest on one another in a tight, upwards coil. Ornamentation consists of large tubercles and ribs. This type of ammonite probably swam with its buoyant shell extended upwards from the tentacled body. The genus grew to about 150mm (6in) in length, and occurs in rocks of Cretaceous age, worldwide. This specimen is from southern England.

AMMONITES AS ZONE FOSSILS

Precise stratigraphy and relative dating of rocks is carried out by using fossils which characterize certain parts of the time scale. The criteria on which zones are established and the choosing of zone index fossils is discussed on page 16. The ammonites give an amazingly precise subdivision of the Jurassic strata. It has been calculated by the use of radiometric dating that the average length of a Jurassic ammonite zone is less than 800,000 years, and the more refined sub-zones are as short as 400,000 years. Like the graptolites, the ammonites evolved rapidly into a variety of easily identifiable genera and species. They also were able to move freely, and their buoyant shells may have drifted widely after death (as does the shell of the modern *Nautilus*). The graptolites, though excellent zone fossils in the dark shales of the Lower Palaeozoic era, had certain drawbacks because of their delicate structure, whereas ammonites, with their comparatively robust shells, are found as fossils in a great variety of sedimentary rocks, from sandstones to shales and limestones. This is also a result of their ability to move through the water and freedom from the sediment forming on the sea bed. Because of these factors, it is possible to correlate different rocks, formed in different environments, by observation of ammonite fossils. Other cephalopods are also used as zone fossils – for example, goniatites, which are important for identifying strata of the Devonian and Carboniferous periods.

▽ Sigaloceras

This fossil ammonite is preserved in pyrite, a common mode of preservation. Small nodules of this mineral are stuck to the shell. The ornamentation of this involute shell consists of fine ribs, some of which are stronger than others. Suture lines are clearly visible on the specimen shown. This is a genus in which sexual dimorphism is recognized. The microconch has a lappet. *Sigaloceras* grew to about 60mm (2³/₈in) in diameter (microconch) and 100mm (4in) diameter (macroconch). It occurs in rocks of Upper Jurassic age, worldwide. *Sigaloceras caloviense* is a zone fossil.

△ Hoplites

This ammonite shell has sub-involute coiling, the inner whorls being virtually hidden by the outer whorl. In this specimen the outermost whorl has sutures to its margin so another whorl may be missing. The shell is ornamented with stout main ribs, with secondary ribs between them. There is a smooth band running around the venter. Tubercles are often developed near the umbilical margin, and the ribs curve forwards towards the ventral surface. *Hoplites* grew to about 90mm (3¹/₂in) in diameter, and occurs in Cretaceous strata in northern Europe. This ammonite genus is found with a variety of other fossils including other ammonites, belemnites, echinoids and occasionally marine reptiles. *Hoplites dentatus* is a zone fossil.

▽ *Endemoceras*

This small ammonite has sub-involute coiling. The whorls become rapidly larger towards the aperture, and they are ornamented with stout ribs which split before crossing the venter. This specimen is of typical size at 40mm (1^5/$_8$in) in diameter. *Endemoceras* is from rocks of Lower Cretaceous age in Europe. The strata in which it is found are rich in belemnites and other molluscs.

△ *Mantelliceras*

The sub-involute shell of this ammonite is ornamented with thick ribs, which develop two rows of tubercles where they cross the venter. This is broad and the whorl section angular. The umbilical margin has smaller tubercles.

Mantelliceras grew to about 100mm (4in) in diameter, and occurs in Cretaceous strata in Texas (USA), Europe, North Africa, India and Southeast Asia. It is found with a number of other ammonites, and bivalves.

◁ *Euhoplites*

The coiling of this shell is sub-involute, and there is a deeply set umbilicus. There are stout, forwards-sweeping ribs with prominent nodes near the venter. The ventral surface has a slight groove that interrupts the ribs. Nodes may also be present on the umbilical margin. This genus grew to about 50mm (2in) in diameter, and is found in rocks of Lower Cretaceous age in Greenland, Alaska and northern Europe. The pictured specimen is from Kent, UK. It is found with various other fossils including the ammonites *Hamites* and *Anahoplites*, bivalves, corals, belemnites, gastropods, scaphopods and arthropods. *Euhoplites latus* is a zone fossil.

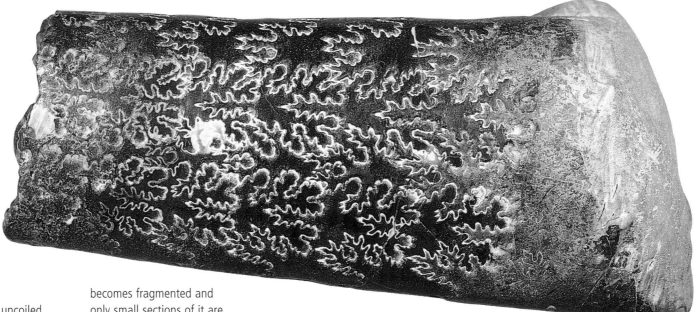

△ **Baculites**

This ammonite has an uncoiled shell of almost oval cross-section, that is similar in outward appearance to the orthocone nautiloids of the Palaeozoic era. However, the complex suture lines, clearly visible on this specimen, easily distinguish this genus. In its early development this ammonite is coiled, only later developing a straight shell. The shell often becomes fragmented and only small sections of it are fossilized, as shown here. Ornamentation consists of ribs and tubercles on the ventral surface, and a rostrum develops at one side of the aperture. *Baculites* reached 2m (78in) in length and is found in Upper Cretaceous rocks, worldwide. This specimen is from South Dakota, USA.

◁△ **Scaphites**

This ammonite has a partially uncoiled shell structure. One of the pictured specimens (above) is complete, the other is broken and retains only the inner whorls (left). The outer whorl of this genus is large compared with the rest of the shell, and is the most uncoiled. It is involute and broad and flattened. The aperture has a hooked structure and faces the rest of the shell. Ornamentation consists of closely spaced ribs, with nodes near the venter and the umbilical margin. This ammonite is strongly dimorphic. It grew to about 50mm (2in) in width and occurs in strata of Cretaceous age in North America, southern Africa, Chile, Australia, Madagascar and Europe. The complete specimen is from South Dakota, USA.

△ Hamites

Hamites is an ammonite genus with an atypical shell shape. When complete it forms an open uncoiled shell. This is in a number of distinct sections, often with three straight parts joined by hook-shaped curves. Commonly it is broken into small fragments such as those in the photograph. The shell cross-section is round or oval, and it is ornamented with strong, encircling ribs. In some species these are interrupted on the dorsal surface. *Hamites* grew to about 65mm (2½in) in length, and occurs in rocks of Lower Cretaceous age in North America, Europe and Asia. It is found with other ammonites including *Anahoplites* and *Euhoplites*, bivalves such as *Nuculana*, the scaphopod *Dentalium*, gastropods such as *Pleurotomaria*, belemnites and vertebrate remains.

◁ Laevaptychus

These fossils have often been found in the body chamber of ammonites. Their exact purpose has been the subject of much discussion. They used to be considered as opercula – doors on the aperture – behind which the ammonite creature could withdraw. They are now believed to be part of the ammonite lower jaw. One surface is concave and ornamented with concentric ribs, while the other is convex and smooth. These jaw structures are similar to those of modern coleoids, the group of molluscs including the squids. The photograph of *Arnioceras* (page 137) shows one of these structures in the shell aperture. The examples shown are 60mm (2³⁄₈in) in width. Their size varies according to the ammonite to which they are related. They are found in Jurassic strata, worldwide.

△ Anahoplites

This genus has a compressed, flattened shell, with highly involute coiling. The umbilical margin is steep. Ornamentation consists of thin ribs with secondaries between them near the venter. This is flattened and has a slight groove in its centre with corded margins. Slight nodes are sometimes seen near the umbilical margin. This genus grew to about 100mm (4in) in diameter, and it is found in rocks of Lower Cretaceous age in Europe and Asia. It occurs with a variety of other ammonites, bivalves, gastropods and belemnites.

▽ Ammonite jaw

This specimen from the Upper Jurassic period is one of the rare cases in which the jaw mechanism of an ammonite is preserved. These structures are more similar to those of modern squids than to those of *Nautilus*.

BELEMNITES

Belemnites are an extinct group of cephalopods that belong to the sub-class known as the coleoids. This sub-class is closely related to the ammonoids, and includes the squids, octopods and cuttles, which are well known in modern oceans. Belemnites are common fossils, particularly in marine strata of Mesozoic age, although they are sometimes found in rocks as old as Lower Carboniferous and as young as the Tertiary era. These strange fossils are made up of two separate structures, which are often found isolated from each other. The soft body of the living belemnite fitted around a thick, bullet- or cigar-shaped internal shell with a sharply pointed end. If complete, this part of the belemnite fits into a separate chambered part, known as the phragmacone. The belemnite was a squid-like creature with tentacles, eyes and an ink sac. Their fossils are difficult to collect because they break easily. Most are fairly small but they can grow to 200mm (8in) in length. Belemnites have similar features to other cephalopods including their ability to swim freely, which makes them useful zone fossils.

◁ **Actinocamax**
This genus has a lance-shaped guard. The surface is ornamented with thin lines. There is a groove running along the ventral part of the fossil. The surface of this guard is often granular, and it may retain impressions left by the attachment of vascular tissue. This belemnite is about 75mm (3in) in length, and occurs in rocks of Upper Cretaceous age in Greenland, Europe and Asia. It is found with a variety of other fossils, including ammonites, bivalve molluscs and echinoids. The pictured species, *Actinocamax plenus*, is used to mark a sub-zone of the Upper Cretaceous period.

▷ **Belemnitella**
This common cylindrical genus is ornamented with grooves and thin lines. These diverge near the apex which has a definite separate tip. Vascular impressions and granular markings are often present. In the anterior end there is a deep notch that slopes from the ventral surface. This genus grew to about 150mm (6in) in length, and is found in Upper Cretaceous strata in North America, Europe, Asia and Greenland. *Belemnitella mucronata* is a zone fossil.

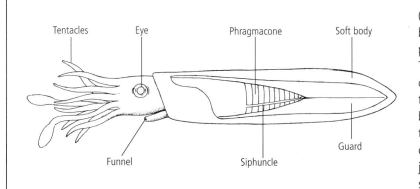

△ **Belemnite ink sacs**
These illustrations of belemnite ink sacs were drawn with ink reconstituted from the fossils. They appear in *The Bridgewater Treatise* by William Buckland, published in 1836.

◁ **Acrocoelites**
This photograph shows a great number of guards of *Acrocoelites*, a belemnite from the Lower Jurassic rocks of North America and Europe. The shale bedding plane reveals the orientation of these fossils with their long axes parallel. They were probably orientated in this way by currents flowing along the sea bed. The majority of these shells are broken, but in a few the end of the phragmacone can be seen inside the blunt end of the guard, where the fossil has split lengthwise. This genus grew to about 120mm (4³/₄in) in length.

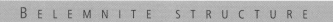

BELEMNITE STRUCTURE

Tentacles · Eye · Phragmacone · Soft body · Funnel · Siphuncle · Guard

The calcareous guard (internal shell) of the belemnite is usually the only part to be found as a fossil. The phragmacone is a chambered structure within the guard. In life the soft body was wrapped around the guard. This squid-like creature was able to swim by jet propulsion and could also squirt out a defensive cloud of ink.

11 VERTEBRATES

This large group of fossils includes the remains of fish, amphibians, reptiles, birds and mammals. For a number of reasons fossils of these creatures are not as common as those of invertebrates. Many invertebrates live in the sea and so their shells and skeletons are rapidly covered with sediment when they die. This sediment is often undisturbed and eventually forms stratified sedimentary rock, containing fossils. Moreover, invertebrates existed for many hundreds of millions of years before the development of vertebrates.

Some vertebrate groups such as fish and marine reptiles lived in the sea and were readily fossilized, but the major land-dwelling vertebrate groups were less frequently buried by sediment after death. Weathering and erosion are dominant forces on land and only occasionally does a skeleton, or a few of its bones, become trapped in the sand of a river bank or lake. However, there are some areas – for example, in North America, Africa and China – where large numbers of vertebrate skeletons have become fossilized in lake and river deposits. Whole skeletons are very rare, and often only a single tooth or bone fragment is all that is left of a once huge creature.

THE FIRST FISH

The first vertebrates to occur as fossils date from the Cambrian strata of Wyoming, USA. These are small fragments of bone, and are about 500 million years old. The scanty remains are of a group of fish called the Agnatha. They were jawless fish and developed during the Ordovician, Silurian and Devonian periods. These first vertebrates were in some respects like modern lampreys and hag-fish, which are thought to be their descendants. They had a simple hole for a mouth and probably grubbed about in the bottom mud for food. Many of the early fish – for example, *Cephalaspis* – lived in brackish and fresh water, and occur as fossils in rocks of Devonian age. One group of jawless agnathans, called the Osterostrachi, had a strongly armoured body, with bony material for protection. The head was very flat with a bony shield covering it. This had holes for the eyes and a single nostril, and gill slits beneath.

◁△ **Bone bed**
Numerous fragments of bones and teeth make up this typical deposit.

Some of the remains are very worn, while others are well preserved.

JAWED FISH

Fish with jaws took over from the agnathans during the Devonian period. There are four main groups, some of which are still represented today. The Chondrichthyes were abundant in Carboniferous and Permian times and include the shark

genera *Lamna* and *Charcarodon*. Fish with cartilagenous skeletons are included in this group. These often have skin studded with small sharp scales. Lacking a bony skeleton, these fish are often known only from their teeth. The placoderms and acanthodians are two other types of jawed fish. The fourth group, the Osteichthyes or bony fish, appeared in the Devonian period and gave rise to many modern fish.

Possibly the most important of the Osteichthyes are the teleosts, which date from the Jurassic period. They are represented today by over 25,000 fish species in all types of aquatic habitats. The actinopterygian fish – those with ray fins – and the bony-plated holosteans also belong to the Osteichthyes. Other bony fish include the dinopan, or lung-fish, and the crossopterygians. The latter are of particular interest because their vertebrae are similar to those of the early amphibians.

AMPHIBIANS

Amphibians developed from fish during the Devonian period. The earliest tetrapod (four-legged creature) is found in the Devonian strata of Greenland. The amphibians flourished in the luxuriant swamp forests of the Carboniferous period. They depended on water for reproduction, and many of them were equipped with sharp teeth, possibly for catching fish. The temnospondyl (page 167) is from the Carboniferous period

▽ **Holoptychius**
This fish has a number of characteristic features. The fins are lobed and they have dermal bones. The body has a coating of large rounded scales, which are easily seen in these fossils. The tail is described as heterocercal, meaning that there are vertebrae in the upper lobe; the lower lobe is smaller. These two specimens are from Dura Den, in Fife, Scotland, where there are sediments of river and possibly shallow-marine origin. *Holoptychius* grew to about 500mm (20in) in length and occurs in rocks of Devonian to Lower Carboniferous age.

and is the earliest complete fossil of an amphibian. Modern amphibians such as frogs, newts and salamanders do not appear in the fossil record until Triassic times.

REPTILES

The earliest reptiles are known from fossils found in rocks of Middle Carboniferous age. These creatures had developed a reproductive system which allowed them to break free from the watery environment required by their amphibian antecedents. This evolutionary breakthrough was the amniote egg that protected the developing embryo and did away with the need for a larval stage. Possibly the best known of the ancient reptiles are the dinosaurs. Bones of these varied and very successful creatures are found in rocks of Jurassic and Cretaceous age in many parts of the world, including North America, China, Central Asia, Australia, Africa and Europe.

◁ **Glyptolepis**
This specimen is well preserved in an iron-rich concretion. The body is covered with large scales, which are thin and rounded. They often have tubercles and ridges on their surfaces. *Glyptolepis* is a bony fish that lived in fresh water. The whole body was elongated with the paired fins set well back near the tail. The upper lobe of the tail was larger than the lower one. Only the front part of the creature is seen here. If it were complete, this specimen would be about 150mm (6in) in length. *Glyptolepis* is found in strata of Devonian age, worldwide. This specimen is from Nairn, Scotland.

The bones of *Iguanodon* (page 168) are from one of the first dinosaurs to be described. The word 'dinosaur' means terrible lizard. It was first used by the British anatomist Sir Richard Owen in 1842, and since that time these large creatures have captured the popular imagination. Dinosaurs are thought to have developed from a more primitive group of reptiles called the thecodonts which evolved during the Carboniferous period. The crocodiles are another reptile group that developed from the thecodonts.

There are three main groups of dinosaurs. The theropods are the large carnivorous dinosaurs. These have two strong walking legs and atrophied front limbs. One of the best known members of this group is *Tyrannosaurus*. This flesh-eating dinosaur has been found fossilized in rocks of Cretaceous age in North America and Central Asia. It may have lived both by killing prey and by scavenging. Like other theropods, it had very small front legs, in this case with only two small claws. *Tyrannosaurus* grew to over 14 metres (46ft) in length.

▽▷ *Gyroptichius*

This fish is characterized by its diamond-shaped scales, which are seen in close-up. The specimen has large scales, and plates covering the head. The fossil is virtually complete. It has a short, stumpy tail centrally positioned around the spinal vertebrae and two sets of paired fins towards the rear of the body. This genus is thought to have swum rather like an eel, with a wriggling movement of its tapering body. It lived in non-marine waters, and grew to about 70mm (2³/₄in) in length. It occurs in rocks of Devonian age, worldwide. *Gyroptichius* fossils are found with those of a number of other fish, including *Glyptolepis*, *Dipterus* and *Cheirolepis*. This specimen is from Orkney, Scotland.

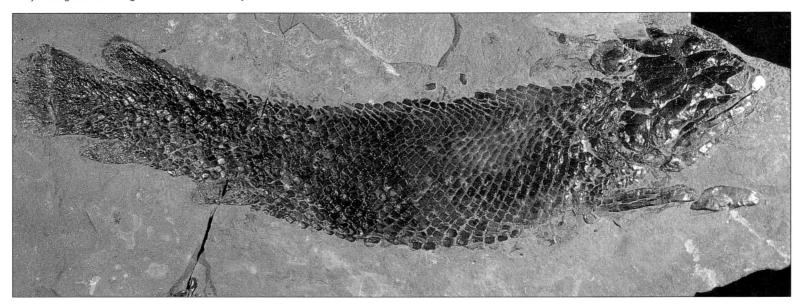

▷ *Ischnacanthus*

One of the first truly jawed fish, *Ischnacanthus* has a mouth filled with numerous small teeth. It is characterized by spines on the dorsal and ventral surfaces, which are well preserved in the pictured specimen. There are two on the back and three beneath. The body is stout and tapers gradually to the tail. This fish lived in fresh water. *Ischnacanthus* grew to about 60mm (2³/₈in) in length, and is found in rocks of Devonian age, worldwide.

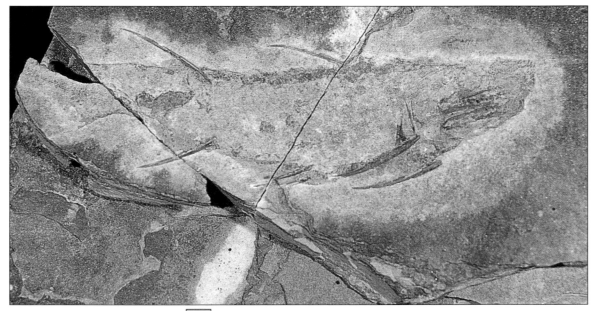

The sauropodomorphs include the giant herbivorous dinosaurs like *Brachiosaurus*, *Diplodocus* and *Apatosaurus* (formerly known as *Brontosaurus*). These are characterized by their huge bodies, which in some genera weighed over 30 tonnes, long heavy tails and necks, and small heads. The large body was supported by stout legs. The popular view of these creatures wading in swamps and marshes to give further support to the heavy body is now considered inaccurate by many researchers. The structure of the skeleton, especially the strong back, indicates a land-based lifestyle. It has been argued that the pressure of the water at depths of over 10 metres (33ft) would have been too great to allow their lungs to expand.

The third group are the ornithischians. These may be either bipedal or quadrupedal, and include herd-living herbivores. *Iguanodon* is an example. Some ornithischians are large – *Iguanodon* was over 10 metres (33ft) long – while others such as *Hypsilophodon* were small, at only 2 metres (6½ft) long. Some ornithischian genera developed heavy bony plates or

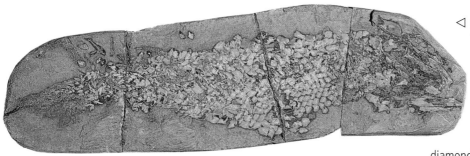

◁ **Osteolepis**
This genus of fish has a tapering body with two dorsal and three ventral fins. The lobes of the tail are unequal, the upper lobe being larger. Its body is covered with small diamond-shaped scales and the head is protected with larger scales and plates. The mouth is filled with many small, sharp teeth, which suggests that this fish may have been a carnivore. It lived in fresh water, and is found fossilized with other fish including *Cheirolepis*. *Osteolepis* grew to about 120mm (4³/₄in) in length, and occurs in rocks of Devonian age in Europe and Asia.

▷ **Cephalaspis**
The characteristic features of this fish are its very large head-shield, which curves backwards with pointed extensions, and its thin eel-like body. The head has small eye holes centrally placed on the upper surface. The small mouth is underneath. It probably fed by sifting the sediment and suction feeding. There are gill slits behind the mouth. The elongated shape of the body suggests that it may have moved by wriggling. This jawless fish belongs to one of the earliest vertebrate groups. Detailed research has been carried out into the structure of the brain of these fish. From such work it has been determined that the cephalaspids had a brain very similar to that of the modern lampreys, a group of primitive, eel-like, parasitic fish. *Cephalaspis* grew to about 100mm (4in) in length, and is found in rocks ranging in age from Upper Silurian to Middle Devonian, worldwide.

◁ **Cheirolepis**
This fish belongs to the actinopterygian group of ray-finned fish, whose fins are supported by strengthening rays. This group gave rise to the teleosts which are the dominant fish group today. *Cheirolepis* is a slender fish. This specimen from Clune, Scotland, is almost complete. There are small, square scales covering the body and a single large dorsal fin. The upper lobe of the tail is larger than the lower one. This genus grew to about 350mm (14in) in length, and occurs in rocks of Middle and Upper Devonian age, worldwide.

◁ *Bothriolepis*

The photograph shows only the head and the two long appendages that project from the head shield. These are the parts most commonly fossilized. Large armoured plates cover the head, and the appendages are similarly protected. These are mobile and articulate at the sides of the head shield. Behind the part shown here there would have been a slender, scale-free tail. This tail had a large upper lobe and a smaller lower one. *Bothriolepis* belongs to the group called the placoderms. These fish are characterized by simple jaws and paired fins. They probably lived on the bottom mud in fresh-water lakes. Their heavy armour may have been defence against predators such as the large eurypterids, including *Pterygotus*. The specimen shown is about 90mm (3¹/₂in), long and is from Scaumenac Bay, Canada. *Bothriolepis* can be found in Devonian rocks, worldwide.

◁ *Platysomus*

This modern-looking fish has been wonderfully preserved in fine-grained limestone. It is an actinopterygian, with fins that are triangular and unpaired. The long scales that cover the main part of the body extend from top to bottom, as seen in the photograph. The body of *Platysomus* is very deep and the tail has lobes of equal size. Platysomids were agile swimmers and had conical teeth. This specimen is about 70mm (2³/₄in), long. The genus is found in rocks of Lower Carboniferous to Permian age, worldwide. The specimen is from the Permian Marl Slate of Durham, UK. This deposit is well known for its fine fish fauna.

▷ *Dipterus*

This fish is a member of the dinopan group which contains the lung-fish. Like other dinopans, it has a thick-set body. Most of the fins are near the tail on the dorsal and ventral surfaces, with smaller fins just behind the head on the ventral surface. The tail is heterocercal, with a larger upper lobe that contains the vertebral column. The jaws of *Dipterus* have flattened teeth in the palate and floor of the mouth that are used for crushing small invertebrates. Many early fish were subjected to river conditions which fluctuated and sometimes died together in large numbers when the water was very low. Some fish, such as *Dipterus*, were able to withstand drought and could utilize oxygen in the atmosphere. The lung-fish were so called because they evolved a 'lung' that enabled them to survive in mud when the water dried up. Modern lung-fish are able to burrow and survive for considerable periods out of water. Other features such as the strong bony strengthening of the fins help the lung-fish to crawl on land. *Dipterus* grew to about 70mm (2³/₄in) in length, and occurs in Middle Devonian strata, worldwide. The specimen is from the Achnaharras fish beds of Scotland.

tubes on their skulls. *Corythanosaurus* had a crest filled with breathing tubes, while *Triceratops* had a heavily armoured plate with horns. Two other types of reptiles are often found as fossils. These are the sea-dwelling ichthyosaurs and plesiosaurs, and the flying pterosaurs.

There is no satisfactory widely accepted explanation for the extinction of the dinosaurs. This was not as sudden as is often suggested and may have been a gradual event lasting half a million years or more. The dinosaurs were not the only creatures to die out at the end of the Cretaceous period. Over 75 per cent of the marine plankton, as well as successful creatures like the ammonites, also failed to make it into the Tertiary era. Any theory about the death of the dinosaurs has to account for the survival of many other groups of creatures. These include the mammals, cuttlefish and *Nautilus*, birds and lizards. A modern suggestion is that a large meteorite hit the Earth and as a result debris filled the sky and blocked out sunlight. Plant growth was reduced for many years and the food chain was thus upset. A similar theory says that a meteorite came quite close to the Earth and produced high temperatures and poisoned the atmosphere. The meteorite idea is backed up by the existence of a thin band of clay, at the right point in the time scale, which contains uncommonly high levels of the rare metal iridium. This, so it is argued, came from the meteorite. Another well-documented theory suggests that the lowering of the sea level at the end of the Cretaceous period could be a possible cause of the extinctions. Creatures and plants living in shallow water and near to the sea coast would have suffered most. Another result of this would have been a rise in temperature, because of the reduced surface area of the seas. Evidence for this rise in temperature is provided by isotopes of oxygen found in limestones of the time. It may be that a number of factors including some of these were involved. What is certain is that the end of the Cretaceous period saw the spread of the mammals as the dominant life-form on land.

THE AGE OF THE MAMMALS

The earliest mammals were small shrew-like creatures, and during the Jurassic and Cretaceous periods these developed only slowly. They are rare as fossils because they lived on land and were small. In the Tertiary era, however, partly because of the demise of the large reptiles, many habitats could be exploited by the mammals and a great variety evolved. Some of these grew to enormous size. *Indricotherium*, for example, was like a giant rhinoceros and reached a height of over five metres (16ft) at the shoulder. Types of mammals developed that were able to take advantage of the abundant grasslands – for example, the early horses and their relatives. These were themselves preyed on by the carnivores. Around 20,000 years ago a mass extinction destroyed many of these diverse

mammals, including the mammoths, giant elks and sabre-tooth tigers. Some may have been killed off by early man, but the real causes are unknown.

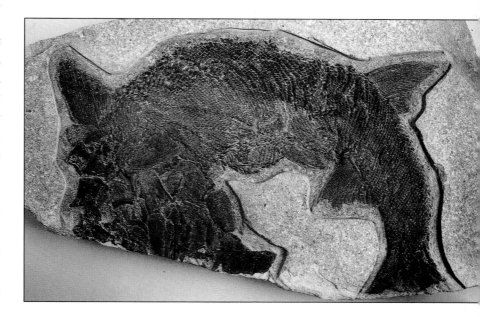

△ **Acrolepis**
This specimen is almost complete with only part of the head and tail missing. It is preserved in similar rock to the fossil of *Platysomus*. The scales are coarse and diamond-shaped and there are pelvic and pectoral fins. The large head is usually about a quarter of the length of the whole fish. *Acrolepis* grew to about 400mm (16in) in length, and occurs in strata of Carboniferous and Permian age in Germany, the CIS, Greenland and Britain.

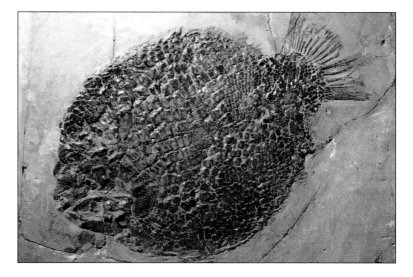

△ **Dapedius**
Holostean fish such as *Dapedius* have bony plates rather than scales on their outer surface. During the Jurassic period they were superceded by the teleosts. This specimen has a characteristic rounded outline, and the large rectangular plates are easily seen. The head is protected by larger plates and has a small mouth filled with sharp, thin teeth. The dorsal fin is long and the tail fan-shaped, with an upper supporting structure. Below the tail is a long anal fin. This genus grew to about 200mm (8in) in length, and is found in Lower Jurassic strata in Europe, often with molluscs, including bivalves and ammonites. The pictured specimen is from southern England.

GREEN RIVER FORMATION

Numerous fossil fish have been perfectly preserved in these famous lake sediments. The lakes originally formed in a series of basins that developed in the eastern Rocky Mountains after tectonic movements at the end of the Cretaceous period. In the Eocene period rivers flowed through these basins and fed lakes, some of which existed for only a short time.

The Green River Formation occupies three distinct basins: The Unita Basin is to the southwest of the Rockies in Utah; the Piceance Basin is to the east in Colorado: the Green River Basin is to the north in Wyoming. These basins contain limestones, some of which have been compared with the Solnhofen *plattenkalk,* and fine-grained detrital sediments, mainly shales, marls and calcareous sandstones. Around the edges of the basins there are coarser rocks such as conglomerates and sandstones. There are also oil shales and evaporites, the latter forming as the waters dried out.

An important feature of the oil shales is that they show very fine layered couplets, about one millimetre (0.04 in) thick. The lower part of each is a layer of silt and the upper part is oily material. These layers are thought to have been formed annually. The silty layer would have formed during the rainy season when more detritus was washed into the basin, and the oily layer formed during the drier season when the only material that fell to the bottom of the lake was organic in origin. By counting these couplets it has been estimated that the lake developed over a period of seven and a half million years.

FOSSIL FINDS

The fossils in the lake sediments include the fish genera *Knightia*, *Gosiutichthys* and *Diplomystus*. There are also insects, ostracods, molluscs and plants. The plants and pollen found in the rocks suggest that the nearby area had a luxuriant vegetation growing in a warm damp climate. The perfect preservation of the fish and other fossils indicates that the waters near the lake bed were stagnant and lacking in oxygen, and that there were no predators.

Collecting fossils from these rocks is a painstaking and technically

▽ **Leptolepis**

This teleost genus exhibits many of the characteristics of modern fish. These are bony fish that have true jaws. *Leptolepis* is a small fish with an elongated, tapering body, having a centrally placed dorsal fin. The small mouth has numerous teeth. The tail has lobes of equal size. It grew to about 120mm (4³/₄in) in length, and is found in rocks of Upper Triassic to Cretaceous age in North America, Europe, Asia and South Africa. *Leptolepis* is well known from the Solnhofen *plattenkalk* of Germany, where it is occasionally found in large numbers.

△ **Diplomystus**

This member of the teleost group fed from the water surface. It has a typical well-formed bony skeleton. There is a single triangular dorsal fin and two smaller fins on the ventral surface. The tail has lobes of equal size. This specimen clearly shows the skeleton but the scales are missing apart from a few of the larger plates that protected the head. The branching nature of the fin supports and the position of the eye are visible. This fish grew to about 500mm (20in) in length. It occurs in Eocene rocks in North America, and is well known from the Green River Formation of Wyoming, USA.

▷ **Gosiutichthys**

In the pictured specimen, this small teleost is preserved as a mass of individuals killed when the lake in which they lived dried out. *Gosiutichthys* was a modern fish, which fed from the water surface. The vertebral column is nearer to the dorsal than the ventral surface. The body tapers to the tail, which has lobes of equal size. It grew to a length of about 500mm (20in). Fossils of this genus occur in rocks of Tertiary age in North America.

demanding business. Once the finely laminated limestone which may contain fish has been located, it is divided into blocks that are separated by trenches. The limestones only split easily when dry and, in order to obtain as many fossils as possible, each thin layer must be examined. Sometimes fossils are found by splitting the thin slabs of rock but this method may slice the fossils in half. The most perfectly preserved fossil fish are those within the fine layers and the preparation of such specimens is very time consuming. It may be possible to locate a fish within a fine layer by looking for the shape it makes on the surface. Low angled sunlight helps with this. Much preparation is required in the laboratory after field collection. This includes delicate scraping with fine pointed tools and airblasting.

The Green River beds are particularly well known for bedding planes covered with great numbers of fossilized fish. These were probably preserved after a mass mortality, possibly caused by the drying out of part of the lake. The specimen of *Gosiutichthys* shown below is of this type.

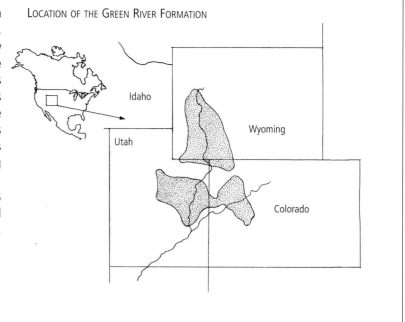

LOCATION OF THE GREEN RIVER FORMATION

▷ Knightia

This herring-like fish is a teleost from the Green River Formation. It has a relatively large head covered with protective plates, but the body scales are not fossilized. The vertebral column is nearer the dorsal surface than that of the deep ventral region. The dorsal fin is triangular and there are pectoral, pelvic and anal fins. The genus grew to about 250mm (10in) in length, and occurs in rocks of Eocene age in North America. Examples of *Knightia*, in which the fossil is fragmented as a result of the explosion of gases inside the rotting carcass, have been found in the Green River Formation.

▽ Odontaspis

These teeth are from an ancient shark with relatives living today that reach over 4 metres (13ft) in length. The teeth have characteristic side cusps (small, sharp points near the base). The fossils shown here are typical, some being complete and others broken. Teeth are composed of durable material and are often fossilized when other materials are not preserved. The teeth shown are about 20mm ($3/4$in) long and they are found in rocks of Cretaceous to Recent age in North America, South America, Europe, Asia, Africa and New Zealand. In strata of Eocene age they are commonly found with many other marine fossils such as gastropods, bivalves, cephalopods and fish.

◁ **Hyaenodon**
This part of the lower jaw comes from the cave hyaena. Such fossils and isolated teeth and bones are sometimes found in sediments and cave Tertiary to Recent age. are adapted for cutting me crushing bones. Early hyaenas small, and in the Eocene period they differed only slightly from insectivores. *Hyaenodon* evolved late in the Eocene period and grew to larger size. This jaw fragment is 80mm (3¹/₈in) long. Many early mammals, including *Hyaenodon*, are fossilized in the Tertiary strata of North America, Europe, Asia and Africa. The modern Striped and Brown Hyaenas live in burrows and caves and are scavengers. Possibly the fossil cave hyaenas followed a similar way of life.

△ **Lamna**
The teeth of this medium-sized shark have a smooth surface that may have vertical striations. Small, sharply pointed cusps occur near the base of the tooth. The overall shape is triangular. Modern species of *Lamna* – the porbeagles – grow to about 4 metres (13ft) in length. The mouth contains three to four rows of teeth, with which it catches a variety of fish, including herrings, sardines, cod and dogfish. It also feeds on cuttles and squids. The modern *Lamna* has wide gill slits, and there is a dorsal fin placed well forward on the dorsal surface. Today these sharks live in cool and temperate seas, frequently swimming in small shoals of about 30 fish. The fossil tooth in the photograph is 30mm (1¹/₈in) long. Fossil remains of this shark are found in strata ranging in age from Cretaceous to Recent, worldwide.

B
R
A
T
E
S

in non-marine
deposits of late
The teeth
t and
were

△ Rhizodus

This large tooth is from a genus of fish which grew to great size. Fossilized lower jaws over a metre (39in) in length have been found. The specimen shown has a typical curved shape and smooth surface. There are grooves in the wider end. It was found in oil shales of Carboniferous age in southern Scotland. These rocks were formed in enclosed basins, with high ground to the south and lava flows to the north, east and west. The specimen is 150mm (6in) long. The fish from which it came is found in rocks of Devonian and Carboniferous age, worldwide.

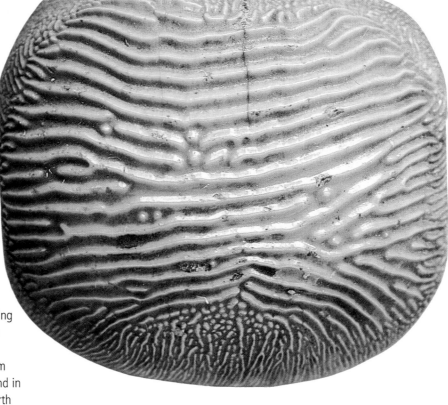

▷ Ptychodus

Sharks of the group known as the ptychodonts have flat teeth adapted for crushing. This fossil is of this type. It is roughly rectangular in shape and has a series of very hard, sharp ridges running across it. Viewed from the side, these teeth have a slightly domed surface with a border of small raised bumps. Teeth like these are virtually all that the fossil record holds of the ptychodonts. The teeth were in paired rows. *Ptychodus* probably fed on shellfish such as bivalves, ammonites and gastropods, using its strong teeth for crushing the shells. This group of sharks survived for tens of millions of years. The fossil shown is 45mm (1³/₄in) wide. This genus is found in strata of Cretaceous age in North America, Europe, Africa and Asia.

▷ *Ceratodus*

This fused tooth is from a fossil lung-fish, closely related to *Neoceratodus*, which lives in Australia today. Lung-fish have a soft skeleton made of cartilage, and the tooth plates are usually the only parts of the creature which are preserved as fossils. *Ceratodus* is a dinopan fish and has a two-fold system for obtaining oxygen. It uses gills when submerged and, when out of water, uses a lung-like air bag which opens into the oesophagus. The surface of the pictured tooth is covered with numerous small dimples that possibly helped to crush food. Modern species feed on both plant and animal matter. *Ceratodus* is found in rocks of Mesozoic age, worldwide. This specimen is 20mm ($^3/_4$in) long. It is from Triassic strata in southern England, where it was found with the teeth and bone fragments of various creatures including *Ichthyosaurus*, *Plesiosaurus* and a number of fish. Some fragments of these bones are visible in the rock containing the specimen.

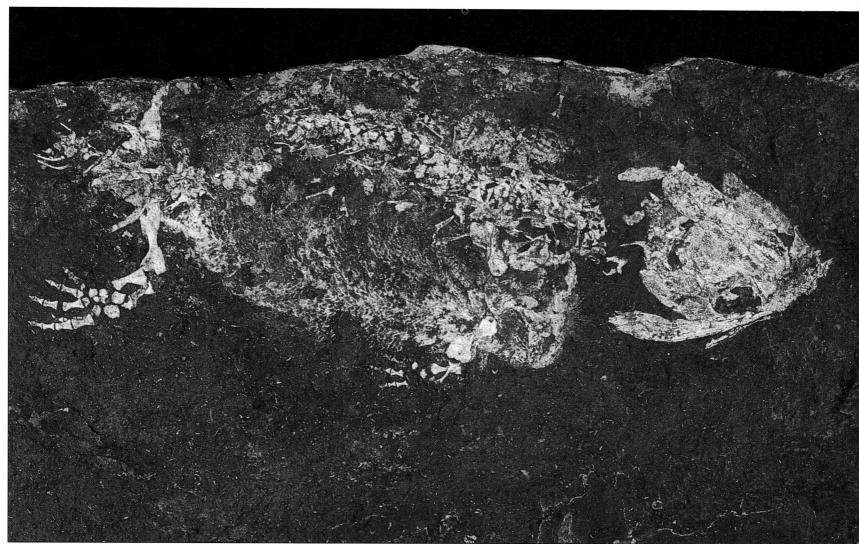

△ *Temnospondyl*

Temnospondyl is not the name of a genus, but is the name of the tetrapod group to which this fossil belongs. This important specimen is the earliest complete skeleton of an amphibian. It is preserved in dark-coloured limestone. The hands have four digits and the feet have five. There is also a tail, and the whole skeleton is in its natural position. A number of incomplete specimens have been found in the same limestone stratum, along with different species of temnospondyl and some other amphibians. The main skeleton has no firm indications that the creature lived predominantly in water. The fact that the fossil was found with invertebrate fauna and no fossil fish supports the idea that temnospondyl probably lived at least partly on land. The earliest creatures of this type, tetrapods, have been found in rocks of Upper Devonian age in Greenland and Australia. They do not become well known in the fossil record until late in the Carboniferous period. This specimen is 400mm (16in) long and was found in the Lower Carboniferous East Kirkton Limestone, in southern Scotland.

IGUANODON

Iguanodon was one of the first dinosaurs to be described. Originally this creature was known only from its fossilized teeth. In 1818 the wife of Dr Gideon Mantell found fossilized teeth near Cuckfield in Sussex, UK. Mantell was a keen fossil collector, but such teeth were very different from anything he had previously found. They seemed to be those of a giant herbivore, but Mantell realized that the Cretaceous strata from which they came were far too old for mammal fossils. The rock stratum was traced to a quarry and Mantell searched for further evidence. At this time the existence of herbivorous reptiles was unknown, but soon Mantell had found some bones from the creature. He also found a spike-like bone which was originally interpreted as a projection from the creature's snout, like that of the iguana. This is now thought to be a thumb spike. Mantell had published a book *The Fossils of the South Downs or Illustrations of the Geology of Sussex* in 1822 and in this he mentioned the fossil teeth, but the creature was not named until 1825, when an anatomist noted their resemblance to those of the iguana.

CHARACTERISTICS AND WAY OF LIFE

Iguanodon was a bipedal ornithopod dinosaur. It walked upright, fed on plants and probably lived in herds. It grew to a height of about 10 metres (33ft). Its body is relatively large and heavy, and balanced by its stout tail

and neck. The strong hind legs were used for walking, but the smaller front legs could be used for locomotion or to allow the creature to rest on all fours. Its large claws are hoof-like, and only the thumb-spike differs. The exact purpose of this, one of the first bones to be discovered by Mantell, has caused much debate. It could have been a defensive weapon and could equally well have dragged vegetation down to the mouth. A notable feature of *Iguanodon* is its long snout, with a toothless, horny, beak-shaped end. The jaws were large and well-equipped with grinding teeth. The snout could have been used for grasping plant material which the grinding teeth chewed before it was passed down to the gut.

The upright posture of *Iguanodon* was originally interpreted following the discovery of many skeletons by miners in a Belgian coal mine in 1878. They came upon a mass of sandstone filled with large bones which were subsequently identified as those of *Iguanodon*. These represented the remains of 30 individuals which had possibly become trapped by a river sandbank, or in a narrow ravine. Among them was the skeleton of a small crocodile, which may have been feeding on the carcasses when it too was engulfed by sand. Correctly reconstructed, the skeletons have an upright posture. The great number found in Belgium is evidence that they lived in herds. *Iguanodon* fossils have also been found in North America and North Africa.

HOW *IGUANODON* MAY HAVE LOOKED

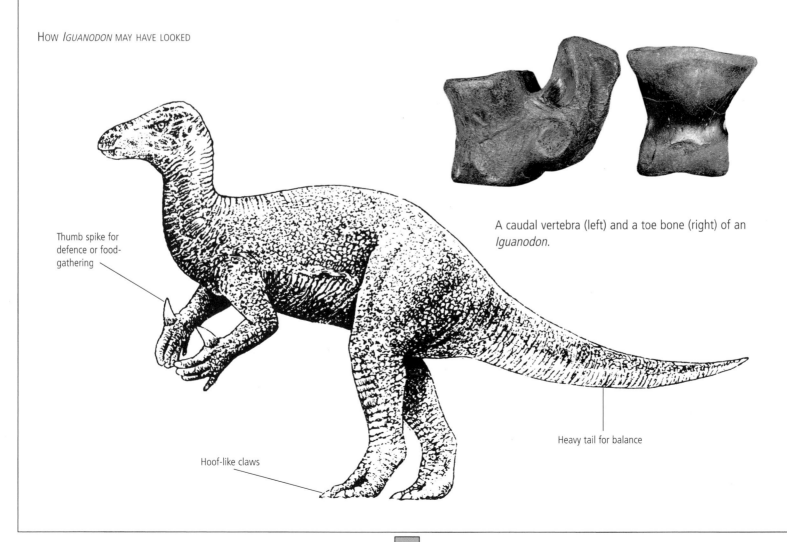

A caudal vertebra (left) and a toe bone (right) of an *Iguanodon*.

Thumb spike for defence or food-gathering

Hoof-like claws

Heavy tail for balance

ICTHYOSAURUS

Ichthyosaurus vertebra

Like modern porpoises, *Ichthyosaurus* had a streamlined body that was well-adapted for fast swimming. It was propelled by paddle-shaped flippers. The long, beak-like snout was probably efficient at catching fish and other marine creatures.

Detail of *Ichthyosaurus* vertebra

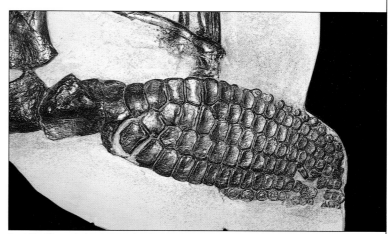

Paddle-like *Ichthyosaurus* limb

The photographs show various fragments of this marine reptile. Our knowledge of this creature comes not only from its bones, but also from a number of fossils that show the carbonized outline of the body around the skeleton. Some whole skeletons even contain young, and one fossil has been found that shows the young dinosaur being born. This is clear evidence that *Ichthyosaurus* did not lay eggs. It has a long beak-like snout filled with sharp conical teeth, with lengthwise grooves. The rounded head contains large eyes, surrounded by a circular series of bones. This structure may have protected the eyes or helped with its focusing. The body and tail are beautifully streamlined and are reminiscent of modern dolphins and porpoises. The limbs have evolved into paddles, and a bony structure supports the ventral lobe of the tail. *Ichthyosaurus* was a carnivorous animal that may have eaten fish and molluscs. Evidence from many fossils indicates that it fed on cephalopods. These molluscs have small hooks on their tentacles which accumulated in the *Ichthyosaurus*'s stomach. One stomach from a relatively small individual contained enough hooks to prove that it had devoured over 1500 cephalopods. *Ichthyosaurus* grew to about 3 metres (10ft) in length, and has a worldwide distribution in rocks of Mesozoic age, where it is often found fossilized with ammonites, belemnites and bivalves.

▽▷ **Plesiosaurus fossils**
The specimens shown include a single vertebra (below), part of a ribcage (below right) and a reconstructed paddle-shaped limb (right).

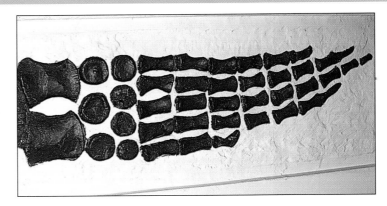

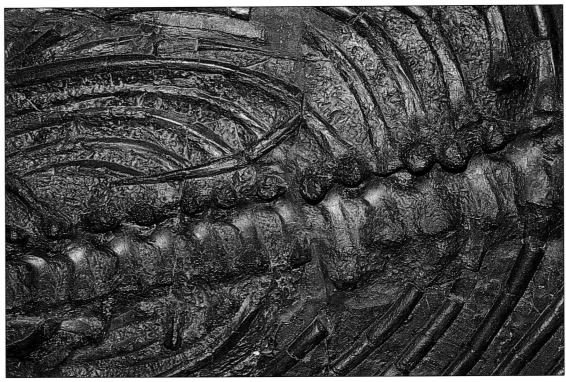

PLESIOSAURUS

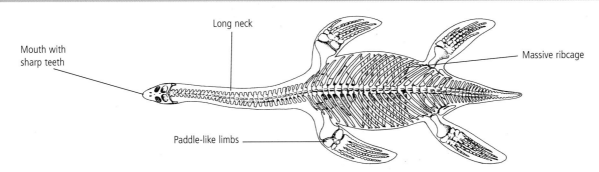

Long neck

Mouth with sharp teeth

Massive ribcage

Paddle-like limbs

This marine reptile has a long thin neck, and large rounded body. The small broad head is equipped with numerous sharp teeth. *Plesiosaurus* had a short tail and four large paddle-shaped limbs. Recent research has shown that the paddles were not moved backwards and forwards but rather they were flapped vertically

rather like the movement of a penguin's wings when it swims underwater. As it swam *Plesiosaurus* possibly used its long neck to 'throw' its head at fish and other prey.

During the 19th century two famous American palaeontologists, Edward Drinker Cope and Othniel Charles Marsh

worked for the US Geological Survey, and were on different expeditions in the 1860s and 1870s. They became bitter rivals for a number of reasons and tried to out-collect each other. Their rivalry may have started in 1868 when Cope gave an account of a newly discovered plesiosaur skeleton. Unfortunately he placed

the head at the end of its tail. Marsh indicated this mistake to the bad-tempered Cope and from then on their relationship was one of criticism and hatred. This rivalry did, however, result in the collection of many tons of exceptional fossils.

◁▽ *Pliosaurus*

In the Jurassic period the plesiosaurs evolved into two groups. One group had a much extended neck, the other group, the pliosaurs, developed a large head and shorter neck. They had very powerful bodies and were similar in some respects to modern killer whales. It has been suggested that they could dive to depths of over 300 metres (1,000ft) searching for cephalopods and other prey. An Australian genus, *Kronosaurus*, has a skull 2.4 metres (8ft) long. In contrast to the small, sharp teeth of the plesiosaurs, the teeth of the pliosaurs were large and blunt. The two groups presumably had different feeding methods, although both were carnivores. Pliosaurs often grew to over 10 metres (35ft) in length, some being far larger. The photographs show two views of a *Pliosaurus* vertebra.

◁ *Crocodile*

This square-shaped bony plate is a scute (horny plate) from the armour-plated coat of a crocodile. It has a rough, pitted surface. Crocodiles are close relatives of the dinosaurs and their scutes and other remains such as teeth are often found as fossils. They evolved late in the Triassic period and survived the late Cretaceous extinctions. Crocodiles have a number of features which have led to their success. They are active on land as well as in the water, and with their eyes and nostrils high on the head they can lie unseen just below the water surface. Their bony armour is an excellent defence, especially for the young. The bony plates on the back are firmly attached to bones and muscles and they help to support these muscles when the animal is walking on land. During the Jurassic period a large number of marine and fresh-water crocodile genera developed. Modern crocodiles first appear toward the end of the Jurassic period. Most fossil crocodiles are between 1 and 3 metres (3$\frac{1}{4}$ to 10ft) long. One giant example from Texas, USA, has a skull nearly 2 metres (6$\frac{1}{2}$ft) long, and could have been 15 metres (50ft) in length.

▽▷ Mammuthus

A foot bone and two views of the cheek tooth of this large, elephant-like mammal are shown. The tooth is 250mm (10in) long and the foot bone 100mm (4in) across. The surface of the tooth is crossed by many rough ridges and furrows. Fossils such as these may be found in river gravels and other sediments, but whole skeletons are rare. As temperatures fell during the Tertiary era, mammals developed that could withstand the new climatic conditions. In the Oligocene period the mean annual temperature in temperate latitudes was 17°C (64°F). It fell during the next period, the Miocene, to around 14°C (57°F). This cooling continued until the Ice Age. The mammoths protected themselves against the colder climate by developing thick coats, a hump of fat, small ears, and increasing their body size. These vast animals migrated south as the ice sheets advanced, and their fossils are found throughout Europe. It seems that they became extinct when the temperatures rose again around 8,000 years ago. They were undoubtedly hunted by early man, and engravings and cave paintings together with frozen mammoth fossils from Siberia provide valuable evidence as to their form.

▷ Mastodon

Only teeth and isolated bones of this elephant-like mammal generally survive. This specimen is of part of the jaw. The teeth have features designed for plant eating. The crowns are fused and high, and continue to grow throughout the animal's life to compensate for the wear of chewing and grinding plant matter. This jaw fragment is 180mm (7¼in) long. *Mastodon* remains are found in rocks of Tertiary age in Europe and North America.

◁ Merycoidodon

This specimen is of the teeth and part of the jaw of this plant-eating mammal. Sometimes referred to as *Oreodon*, it was a pig-like creature. Its remains are common in some parts of North America, especially Wyoming and the Oligocene White River Beds of Nebraska. The molars have four crowns with crescent-shaped cusps. They resemble those of modern cattle. The creature had large upper canine teeth. This fossil is 70mm (2³/₄in) long. Four species have been described, mainly based on size differences.

▽ Balaena

This fossil is of the ear bone of a whale. Such remains are quite common in marine strata of Tertiary age. Whale fossils first appear in the Eocene rocks. These marine mammals developed into a number of different groups, until by the Miocene period the modern types had evolved. There is an outward similarity between the smaller whales and the marine reptiles of earlier geological times; *Ichthyosaurus* for example, has a similar shape to that of modern porpoises. The ear bone illustrated is 55mm (2¹/₈in) in length, and is from Miocene strata.

▷ Charcarodon

Only the teeth from this large shark are commonly found as fossils. They are triangular in shape and diverge into two long roots at the base. There are no side cusps and the edges are serrated. Modern species of *Charcarodon* include the great white shark, *Charcarodon carcharias*. These grow to about 9 metres (30ft) in length. Specimens that reach 6 metres (20ft) weigh about 3 tonnes. The teeth of modern species of this genus are never as large as those of its fossil relatives. The fossil *Charcarodon* probably grew to about 15 metres (49ft) in length. Its teeth are often 150mm (6in) long. It is found in Tertiary strata, worldwide.

▷ Hippopotamus

Native only to Africa today, *Hippopotamus* was widespread in swampy lowland areas during the interglacial periods of the last two million years. The genus first appears in the fossil record in rocks of Pliocene age, and its remains are found in Europe, Africa and Asia. This specimen is of a canine tooth from the lower jaw of this animal. The lower canines are far larger than those in the upper jaw. Large molar teeth are also common fossils. These are of two distinct types. The lower and upper molars have four tubercles, whereas the pre-molars have a simpler structure.

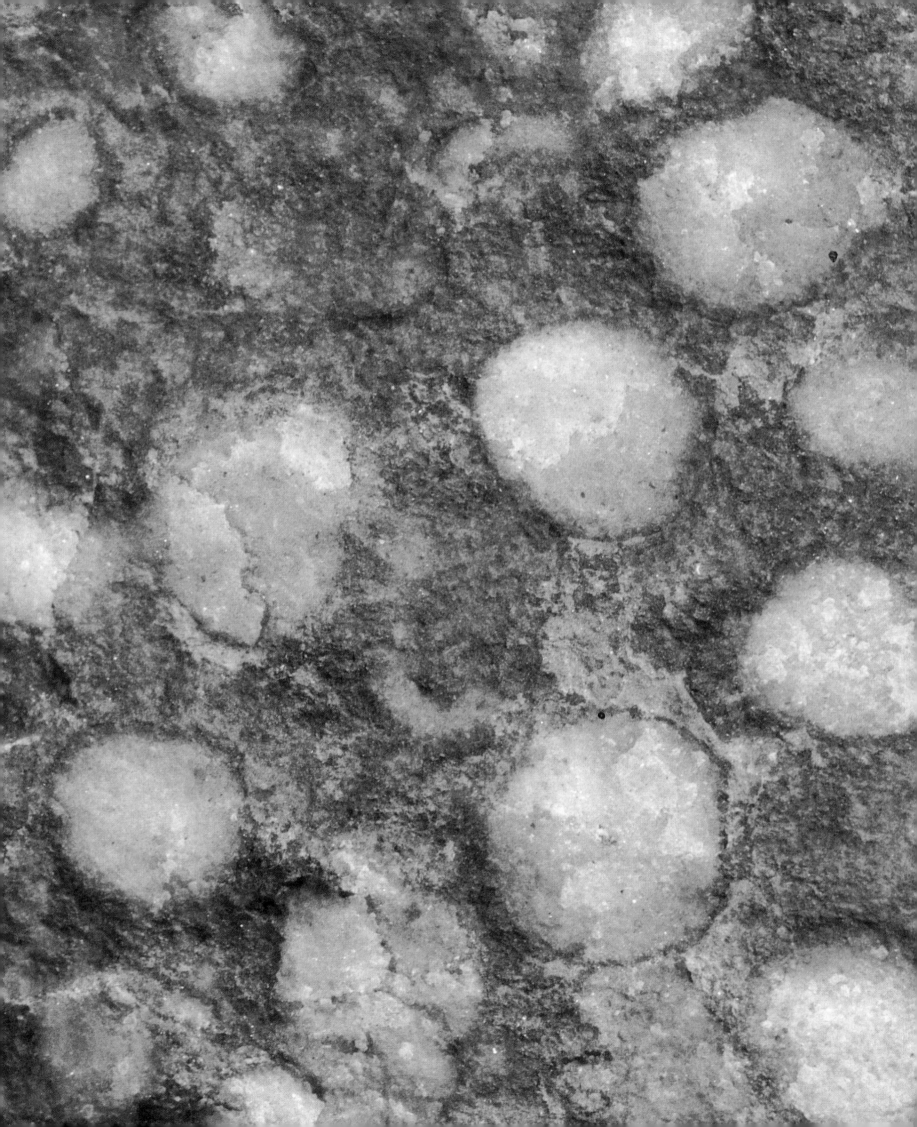

12 TRACE FOSSILS

As well as the fossils of shells, bones and other organic remains, sedimentary rocks contain a great variety of structures that can be attributed to the activity of living creatures. These may occur on the surface of a stratum, or may extend down through a number of rock layers. Such signs of past life are known as trace fossils. They include burrows, tracks, trails, footprints and dung. A great variety of creatures are responsible for these fossils, including worms, molluscs, arthropods and even dinosaurs.

THE PROCESS OF FOSSILIZATION

The actual trace fossil is commonly preserved as a cast or as a mould. A fossilized worm burrow, for example, is a mould, and the sediment or minerals that fill it form a cast. Various creatures make burrows and leave traces of this kind. Worm burrows are common in many formations, such as the Cambrian quartzites of northern Scotland. The worms themselves, being soft-bodied, are not preserved, but the burrows may be infilled with other sediment and make obvious structures in the rock. This is especially true when the infilling material is a different colour from the surrounding sediment.

THE MAKERS OF TRACE FOSSILS

Some burrows are U-shaped and can be mistaken for the mining activity of amphipods (a group of shrimp-like crustaceans). The creature that made a burrow is often unknown, but some can be identified and their remains may even be found in the burrow. The bivalve mollusc *Mya* and its relatives like *Pholadomya* are often found at the bottom of their burrows. *Lingula*, a brachiopod, is another example. Serpulids produce curved burrows that are cemented with calcareous material, while terebellids cement their tubes with shell fragments. Some burrows are not vertical but are made just

▷ **Skolithus**
This is part of a bedding plane crowded with the circular outlines of worm burrows. These burrows have been filled with pale quartz sand, which contrasts with the dark quartzite surrounding them. In some places the greater resistance to weathering of the infilling material may cause burrows like these to stand up slightly above the rock surface. This type of fossil is common in rocks formed in intertidal environments, a typical habitat in which burrowing marine worms live today. The burrows here are 8mm ($^5/_{16}$in) in diameter. The specimen is from Cambrian rocks in Sutherland, Scotland.

◁△ **Worm burrows**
Cross-sections of worm burrows set in a mass of quartzite.

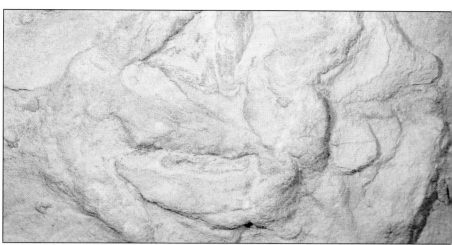

This bipedal dinosaur is known only from its footprints. It lived in muddy marshland of the Jurassic period. The two photographs show a single print and a mass of overlapping prints. They are preserved as positive casts, found when a bedding plane was split. The mould was on the lower surface. The single footprint is 150mm (6in) long. Prints of this type have been found up to 600mm (24in) long. These specimens are from strata of Middle Jurassic age in North Yorkshire, UK.

below the surface of the sea bed. Trails include the markings left on the sea floor by arthropods and molluscs. Some have been attributed to trilobites, others to shrimps and crabs. Gastropods make wandering trails as they graze, and ammonite shells left marks where they rested on the sea bed.

Possibly the most celebrated trace fossils are those left by dinosaurs and other large animals. The study of fossil footprints is called ichnology, and the weight, speed and size of a creature as well as its posture and balance can often be determined. In the Olduvai Gorge in Tanzania the footprints of ancient hominids have been found.

The tracks of a number of different creatures are sometimes found on a single bedding plane. An interesting case of footprints of different sizes on the same rock surface occurs in Dorset, UK. Here the large tracks of the dinosaur *Iguanodon* occur with much smaller, almost human footprints. Did men really live with the dinosaurs? The correct interpretation may be that the smaller markings are those of the dinosaur's smaller front limbs.

THE VALUE OF TRACE FOSSILS

Trace fossils have a number of important uses for the palaeontologist. They are evidence of creatures and how they lived. By comparing a fossil burrow with a modern one, it may be possible to say which type of creature made the burrow. Past ecologies can be established with more detail, and also they help to indicate the orientation of the strata. Many rocks, especially those formed by sedimentary processes, are

DINOSAUR SPEEDS

Many modern creatures of considerable size and weight are able to move at surprising speed. An elephant can move at 40 kph (25 mph), and a hippopotamus can overtake a running man. By studying the trackways and footprints of dinosaurs it can be calculated that many of them were not lumbering giants. The limbs and hip structures of the elephant and rhinoceros are similar to those of some dinosaurs including the ceratopsians. A most important feature of a trackway is the length of the stride. The footprint itself may allow identification of the dinosaur, from clues such as the number and size of the toes or claws, and may give clues to its stance and posture. However, in the determination of the creature's speed, the distance between prints is the most significant factor.

By a study of the way modern creatures move, it is known that the stride length is related to the height of the hips and shoulders. A formula has been worked out that relates stride length to velocity, and this can be applied to any creature, including the dinosaurs. The actual stride length is less important when measuring speed than the relative stride. This is because a small creature moving quickly will have many small strides but a large slow moving creature will take few long strides. Relative stride, used in the formula, is the length of the stride compared with the height of the hips. So if these theories are applied to dinosaur tracks, what speeds are calculated? *Megalosaurus* tracks from Dorset, UK, indicate a speed of 4.3 kph (2.6 mph); carnivores from Texas, USA, have stride lengths suggesting 40 kph (25 mph); adult sauropods from the Paluxy River in Texas moved at 3.6 kph (2.3 mph), while the young were slightly faster at 4 kph (2.5 mph); a large carnivorous dinosaur from Australia moved at 8 kph (5 mph). On the same rock strata are the tracks of some smaller herbivorous dinosaurs. Their speed, across the muddy sediment surface, was as high as 15 kph (9.4 mph).

subjected to folding and faulting, and in some cases they become upturned. Originally sediments are deposited in reasonably horizontal layers on the sea bed or in a similar situation. Because trace fossils are formed on, or from, the original sediment surface when it was the correct way up, by reference to such fossils it is possible to determine if rocks have been upturned.

Trace fossils are named according to the rules of biological nomenclature. It can happen that a burrow and the trail left by an organism are both discovered and given different names. For example, supposed trilobite trails are called *Cruziana*, and the shallow burrows that are more convincingly trilobite trace fossils are called *Rusophycus*. The creature that made the burrow, track or trail has its own name.

▷ **Rotularia**
These fossils are the burrows of polychaete worms, rather than the flattened snail shells they resemble. They are marine bristle worms with segmented bodies. Ragworms, fanworms, catworms and scale worms live freely, but the group called the Sedentaria bore and burrow into rock. The burrowers can produce tubes such as those shown here, strengthened with calcareous cement. These burrows are 15mm (5/8in) in diameter, and are from Eocene strata in Sussex, UK.

▷ **Scolicia**
This sandstone surface is marked with the long sinuous trails left by a grazing gastropod mollusc. The burrow would have been in the soft sea-bed sediment, but is preserved here as a positive feature which infilled the original burrow. These burrows are about 10mm (3/8in) in diameter and the whole specimen is 200mm (8in) across. Such structures are similar to those made by modern sea snails. Fossils such as these are common in rocks ranging in age from Palaeozoic to Recent. The example shown was collected from strata of Carboniferous age in West Yorkshire, UK.

◁ **Imbrichnus**

This is a sediment-filled burrow that winds parallel to the bedding surface. The tubes are sub-cylindrical and some bore slightly into the sediment. Their structure is sinuous and they occasionally wind back in a U shape. The sediment that fills them has a ribbed structure. They are about 10mm ($^3/_8$in) in diameter and were probably formed by a small bivalve mollusc. The specimen is from shallow-marine Jurassic rocks of southern England.

▽ **Lithophaga burrows and polychaete worm burrows**

The older, dark-coloured limestone is of Carboniferous age, and the pale, younger material is the base of the Jurassic system. The older rock has been bored and burrowed by various marine creatures. The bivalve mollusc *Lithophaga* has bored the rounded shapes into the Carboniferous rock. These hollows have been infilled with the Jurassic sediment. The thin tubes are made by polychaete worms. The larger burrows are about 10mm ($^3/_8$in) in diameter. The specimen is from the Mendip Hills of Somerset, UK.

▽ **Thalassinoides**

This specimen shows a bedding plane covered with joined and Y-shaped burrows believed to have been produced by a small crustacean. The area shown is about 120mm ($4^3/_4$in) across. This is a positive cast of the burrows, which were originally made in the soft sea bed. A number of rounded depressions are associated with the burrows. In burrows of this type faecal pellets are occasionally found. The small arthropod *Glyphea* has been found with *Thalassinoides* and may have made these burrows. They are common and occur with a wide variety of fossils, including molluscs and brachiopods in Jurassic strata, worldwide.

◁ **Coprolite**

This is a piece of fossilized excrement deposited by a marine turtle. Such fossils are an important source of information for palaeontologists about a creature's gut and diet. The term coprolite is reserved for larger droppings, whereas the term faecal pellet is used for the smaller waste matter deposited by invertebrates like molluscs and arthropods. The example shown is coated with the hydrated iron oxide mineral, limonite, which gives it a yellowish-brown colour. It is 30mm (1¹⁄₈in) long, but the droppings of larger creatures may be over 400mm (16in) in length. These fossils are found throughout the fossil record, worldwide. This example is from Eocene strata in North America.

▽ **Cruziana**

This specimen from Ordovician rocks at Rennes, France, is of the well-documented trails usually associated with trilobites. This trace fossil consists of parallel grooves and ridges, which may converge. They are often associated with another trace fossil of rounded, bi-lobed shape, called *Rusophycus*. This fossil is almost certainly the impression left by a resting trilobite, and some even retain the impressions of the trilobite appendages. One example is known of a fossil trilobite in the trace fossil.

Although *Cruziana* and *Rusophycus* have been found together, there is some debate among palaeontologists as to whether or not *Cruziana* are the trails of moving trilobites. It has been suggested that the biramous limbs of trilobites, with a walking leg and an upper gill-bearing leg, could not make such trails. The specimen illustrated is typical at 140mm (5¹⁄₂in) in length. Such trace fossils are found in Lower Palaeozoic strata, worldwide.

▽ **Dinosaur eggs**

During the Carboniferous period a new reproductive strategy was developed which allowed the amphibians to break free from the watery environment in which they had previously reproduced. This circumvented the need for a larval stage. The revolution was the amniote egg, so called because of the amnion, a sac of fluid, in which the embryo developed, within the hard outer egg-shell. This closed egg could be laid on land after being fertilized inside the female by the male. The embryo is safe to develop until well-formed and only a few eggs need to be produced compared with the great numbers required when larval stages are involved.

Dinosaurs may have owed at least some of their great sucess to this new means of reproduction. These eggs are from China. They are about 100mm (4in) long and are in a cluster. There are many examples of such 'clutches' of dinosaur eggs. *Protoceratops*, which lived in North America and Asia in the Cretaceous period, left clutches of eggs in concentric arrangement in slight hollows in the ground. The expeditions to the Gobi desert in the 1920s found numerous skeletons of this and other dinosaurs, including adults and recently hatched young. A number of nests were found suggesting that *Protoceratops* may have had colonial breeding behaviour.

AMNIOTE EGG

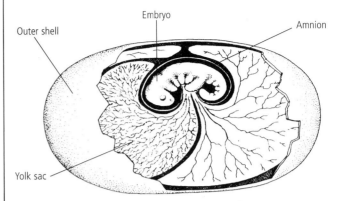

Outer shell · Embryo · Amnion · Yolk sac

This reproductive innovation allowed breeding to take place on dry land. The embryo, enclosed within the membrane known as the amnion, was nourished by the yolk and protected by a hard outer shell.

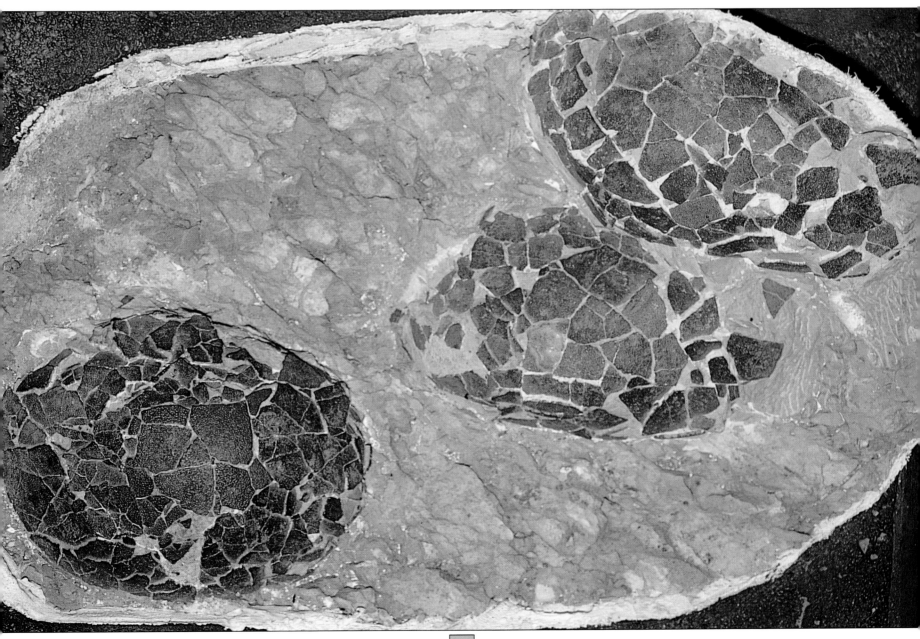

GLOSSARY

Note: This glossary contains a number of words that have everyday meanings as well as a specific usage in relation to fossils. The definitions provided here concentrate on the use of such terms in the context of this book. In the main body of the book anglicized versions of the Latin names for classes and phyla of organisms have generally been used. Both Latin and anglicized versions are given here.

aboral Describes the surface of the test of an echinoid that contains the periproct and anus. In most genera this is the upper surface.

adductor muscles The muscles that close the two valves of a shell, such as that of a brachiopod.

amber Hardened resin from coniferous trees.

ambulacra (singular: ambulacrum) Plates on the test of an echinoid. In the regular echinoids these run in narrow bands around the test from periproct to peristome. In the irregular echinoids the ambulacra may be petal-shaped and atrophied.

ammonites An extinct group of ammonoids that existed during the Jurassic and Cretaceous periods.

Ammonoidea (ammonoids) An extinct order of cephalopod molluscs that includes goniatites, ceratites and ammonites.

anterior Towards the front or head end of an organism.

Anthozoa A class of organisms that includes corals and sea-anemones.

apex The top of the spire of a gastropod shell.

apical system A group of plates surrounding the periproct of an echinoid.

aptychus A curved structure, resembling a bivalve mollusc shell, that is believed to be part of the jaw apparatus of an ammonoid.

Arthropoda (arthropods) A phylum that contains organisms characterized by a segmented exoskeleton. It includes the extinct trilobites. Insects, crabs and lobsters are the best-known modern representatives of the phylum.

Articulata (articulates) A group of brachiopods that are able to move their valves in relation to each other.

Asteroidea (asteroids) A class of echinoderms that includes starfish.

atrophied Stunted or shortened, as in an organism that has diminished in size through the process of evolution.

bedding plane The surface on which sediment is deposited, preserved as a flat layer within a sedimentary rock.

Belemnitida (belemnites) An extinct order of cephalopods that belong to the same sub-class as modern squids and octopods.

benthonic On, or living on, the sea bed.

biconical A shell shape that has an overall appearance of two cones joined together.

bifurcate To branch in two. For example, the ribs on the shell of an ammonite may bifurcate where they cross the ventral surface.

bilateral Two-sided. Organisms with bilateral symmetry have identical halves.

biserial Describing a graptolite stipe with thecae on both sides.

Bivalvia (bivalves) A class of molluscs that includes clams, oysters and tellins.

boss A small protrusion on the test of an echinoid to which a spine is attached.

Brachiopoda (brachiopods) A phylum of two-shelled marine organisms that superficially resemble bivalve molluscs but which have many important differences.

brackish Describing water that is neither fresh nor salt, as in an estuary where fresh water from a river mixes with sea water.

byssus A thin, thread-like material by which some molluscs anchor themselves to the sea bed.

calcareous Containing a high level of calcium carbonate.

calcite A soft, fragile mineral composed of calcium carbonate. It is a major component of limestone. Calcite is formed both organically, as in shells, and inorganically.

calice The depression in the upper part of a corallite in which the polyp lived.

calyx A cup-shaped structure in which an organism may live, as for example on the upper surface of a coral.

Cambrian A time period in the Palaeozoic era that lasted from 600 to 500 million years ago. It is named after Wales where the rocks that characterize the period were first identified.

carapace An exoskeleton or dorsal shell.

Carboniferous A time period in the Palaeozoic era that lasted from 345 to 280 million years ago. The strata of this period contain much coal, hence the name.

carbonization A fossil-forming process whereby only the original carbon in the organism is preserved.

cast A type of fossil formed when an impression left in sediment by an organism is filled in and a replica of its external form is created.

cephalon The head-shield of an arthropod such as a trilobite.

Cephalopoda (cephalopods) A class of molluscs characterized by a shell containing buoyancy chambers. This shell is usually coiled in a plane spiral.

chalk A very fine-grained, white limestone composed almost entirely of microscopic calcite shells of organisms such as cocoliths.

chert A siliceous rock, the material for which may come from organic sources such as the spicules of sponges.

chitin A horny material common in the structure of many organisms. It is a nitrogen-rich carbohydrate with a fibrous structure.

Chordata (chordates) Organisms that have an internal rod-shaped supporting structure, such as a backbone.

cirri Minute prehensile branches on the stems of crinoids.

class One of the ranks in the system of biological nomenclature, a class is a subdivision of a phylum. A class is subdivided into orders.

concretion A rounded lump of rock found in a sediment, often containing a fossil.

coprolite Fossil dung.

corallite An individual coral. It may remain solitary or be joined in a colony.

crenulate Notched. Often the margin of a bivalve mollusc shell has this appearance.

Cretaceous A time period that lasted from 136 to 65 million years ago. The name is derived from 'creta' the Greek word for chalk, which is a characteristic rock sediment of the period.

Crinoidea (crinoids) A class, commonly referred to as sea-lilies, in the phylum Echinodermata. These organisms have a stem and a branching calyx.

crust The thin rocky layer that covers the Earth's surface. The thickness of the crust varies from 8km (5 miles) below the ocean basins to around 80km (50 miles) thick under the large continents.

Crustacea (crustaceans) A class of arthropods that includes crabs, lobsters and woodlice.

cuticle An outer layer or membrane that covers the external surface of many invertebrates.

denticulate Having a toothed appearance.

Devonian A time period that lasted from 395 to 345 million years ago. It is named after Devon in southwest England in which rocks characteristic of this period were first studied.

dimorphism The occurrence, especially in fossils, of two distinct forms of a single species. These are usually interpreted as males and females.

dissepiments Small calcareous plates that thicken the wall of a corallite.

dorsal Relating to the back. The inner surface of the whorl of an **ammonoid** is the dorsal surface.

Echinodermata (echinoderms) A phylum that contains such creatures as echinoids, crinoids and asteroids.

Eocene A sub-division of the Tertiary period that lasted from 53.5 to 37.5 million years ago.

era A large unit of geological time subdivided into a number of periods.

erosion The breakdown of rock material caused principally by the effects of wind, water and ice. Erosion occurs in a number of environments such as river beds, glaciers and on coastlines.

eurypterid A type of arthropod that resembles a large scorpion.

evolute Loose coiling of a cephalopod shell, where the whorls do not obscure one another.

exoskeleton An outside, or external, skeleton.

fern A vascular spore-bearing plant.

flint A type of chert found in nodules and bands in the Cretaceous chalk of western Europe. It is composed of microcrystalline silica.

foramen An opening near or at the beak (umbo) of a **brachiopod** shell.

Foraminifera A group of single-celled marine organisms (protozoans).

gape A permanent opening between the valves of a bivalve mollusc.

Gastropoda (gastropods) A class of mollusc that includes snails and slugs. Many gastropods have a spirally coiled shell.

genus (plural: **genera**) A group of similar organisms that can be further subdivided into species.

glabella The central part of the head of a trilobite, probably where the centre of the nervous system was housed.

Gondwanaland An ancient landmass that eventually divided to form the southern continents, including Antarctica, Africa, South America, Australia and India. It existed during the late Palaeozoic and Mesozoic eras.

goniatites A group of ammonoids that were abundant during the Devonian and Carboniferous periods.

graptolites An class of marine organisms that belongs to the phylum Hemichordata.

growth lines Ridged lines, sometimes very faint, that show earlier positions of the margin of a shell. They give information about how the creature has developed and may provide clues to its age.

gymnosperms A group of plants that bear their seeds in cones.

hermaphroditic Having the sexual parts of both male and female in one organism

heterocercal A description of a fish tail that has the vertebral column in a larger upper lobe.

hexacoral A type of coral in which the septa are arranged in groups of six.

hinge line The margin of a two-valved shell (for example, that of a bivalve mollusc) where it opens and closes.

hinge teeth Structures on one shell of a bivalve mollusc that fit into corresponding grooves on the other shell and so provide a hinge.

ichnology The science of fossil footprints.

Inarticulata (inarticulates) A group of brachiopods that are unable to move their valves in relation to each other.

interglacial The interval between ice advances during a prolonged ice age.

invertebrate Without a backbone. Generally used of creatures that have external shells or other supporting mechanisms.

involute Tight coiling of a cephalopod shell, where the outer whorls obscure the inner ones.

keel A ridge that extends around the ventral surface of a cephalopod shell.

Lamellibranchia An alternative name for bivalve molluscs.

lamprey A fish that has an eel-like body and a mouth adapted for sucking and fixing the creature to stones.

lanceolate Spear- or lance-shaped.

lappet An extension protruding from the aperture of an **ammonoid** shell.

leaching The removal of chemicals, often in a downward direction, from a substance by the action of water.

limestone A sedimentary rock composed of a high proportion of calcium carbonate along with smaller amounts of other materials such as clay and quartz.

lycopod A club-moss plant.

macroconch The larger shell of a dimorphic pair (see **dimorphism**). It is usually interpreted as the female.

marginal On or near the edge of, for example, a shell.

Mesozoic An era of geological time that is subdivided into the Triassic, Jurassic and Cretaceous periods.

mica A silicate mineral characterized by its flaky appeance, bright lustre and comparative softness.

micaceous Containing mica.

microconch The smaller shell in a dimorphic pair (see **dimorphism**). It is usually interpreted as the male.

Miocene A subdivision of the Tertiary peiod lasting from 22.5 to 5 million years ago.

Mollusca (molluscs) A large phylum that contains cephalopods, bivalves and gastropods.

Monoplacophora A class of single-valved molluscs that usually have bilateral symmetry.

mould An impression left in sediment by an organism and later infilled to produce a replica or cast.

Myrapoda (myrapods) A group of small land-dwelling arthropods.

nema A thin thread at the end of a graptolite's stipe.

nodule A rounded lump of rock, often only a few centimetres in diameter, occurring in a sedimentary rock. Nodules of ironstone and calcite often develop in shales and clays. Well-preserved fossils may be found in these structures.

oolith A small grain of calcareous sediment with a concentric layered structure. Oolitic limestone is composed of these grains.

operculum A shell that acts as a lid.

oral Relating to the mouth. The oral surface of the **test** of an echinoid is that on which the mouth is sited, usually the lower surface.

Ordovician A subdivision of the Lower Palaeozoic era that lasted from 500 to 440 million years ago.

orthocone Describes a straight cephalopod shell.

ossicle A single plate from the stem of a crinoid.

oxycone A flattened ammonoid shell with a sharp ventral surface.

Palaeocene A subdivision of the Tertiary period that lasted from 65 to 53.5 million years ago.

Palaeozoic The geological time zone that contains the Cambrian, Ordovician, Silurian, Devonian, Carboniferous and Permian periods. It is usually divided into the Upper and Lower Palaeozoic eras, with three periods in each division.

pallial line The line on the inside of a bivalve mollusc shell that joins the adductor muscle scars.

pedicle valve The larger of the two valves in a brachiopod shell that contains the pedicle opening.

Pelecypoda An alternative name for bivalve molluscs.

pentameral Five-fold, as in the pentameral symmetry of regular echinoids.

period A unit of geological time. Periods are generally of less than 100 million years duration. An era is comprised of a number of periods.

periproct The flexible arrangement of small plates surrounding an echinoid's anus.

peristome The group of plates surrounding an echinoid's mouth.

Permian A time period that lasted from 280 to 225 million years ago.

petaloid Petal-shaped, particularly of echinoid ambulacra.

phragmacone Part of the internal shell of a belemnite.

phylum A rank in the system of biological classification below 'kingdom' and above 'order'.

pinnate A leaf consisting of leaflets arranged on either side of a central stem.

pinnules Small alternating structures on the sides of a crinoid's arm. They give the arms a feathery appearance.

placoderms An extinct class of jawed fish that were characterized by external armoured plates.

planktonic Near the surface of the sea.

Pleistocene The earliest part of the Quaternary era, lasting from 2 to 0.1 million years ago and characterized by widespread glaciation.

polyp A soft-bodied organism such as a coral or sea anemone.

Porifera The phylum that contains the sponges.

porous Having pores, or a surface through which fluids can penetrate.

posterior The direction towards the rear of an organism.

Pre-Cambrian The period of geological time before 600 million years ago. Very few fossils are found in rocks of this age.

protoconch The initial small part of a shell. In the **cephalopods** this is in the very centre.

pygidium The tail segments of an arthropod's exoskeleton.

pyrite A crystalline form of iron sulphide that is common in many sedimentary rocks, especially shales and clays, where it can form nodules. Many fossils are composed of this mineral.

quartz A common mineral composed of silicon dioxide. It is hard and shiny, and often forms perfect hexagonal crystals.

quartzite A sedimentary rock containing a high percentage of quartz.

Recent The period of geological time from 0.01 million years ago to the present day.

rhabdosome The whole of a graptolite colony.

septum (plural: **septa**) The internal partitions that separate the chambers in a mollusc shell or a coral.

serpulid Small worms that secrete a twisted calcareous tube.

Silurian A period of time that lasted from 440 to 395 million years ago.

siphon A soft tube that extends from the body of a mollusc to the outside of the shell.

siphuncle A thin tube that runs from the body chamber to the innermost coil of the shell in a cephalopod.

spicules The skeletal parts of a sponge. These can be calcareous or siliceous.

stipe The long part of a graptolite structure on which the **thecae** are situated.

strata (singular: **stratum**) Layers or 'beds' of sedimentary rock.

suture A line of joining. The cephalopods have suture lines where the internal septa meet and join the inner surface of the shell wall. These vary in their complexity in the different groups of this class.

system The rocks deposited during a geological period. The Jurassic system refers to the various rock strata deposited during the Jurassic period.

tabulae The horizontal divisions of a coral.

teleost A modern type of bony fish. These fish have a symmetrical tail and a skeleton covered with skin.

Tertiary A time period that lasted from 65 to 2 million years ago.

test The shell of a creature, especially used of echinoids.

thecae The cup-like structures on a graptolite stipe.

thorax The main body part of an organism.

trace fossil A fossil that contains no part of the organism to which it relates. It may be, for example, a footprint, a burrow, a **coprolite** or egg.

Triassic The period of geological time that lasted from 225 to 190 million years ago.

umbilicus The centre of a coiled shell.

umbo (plural: **umbones**) The beak-like part of a bivalve or brachiopod shell.

uniserial Describing a graptolite stipe with thecae on one side only.

vascular Having veins.

ventral surface The underside of an organism. The opposite of dorsal.

ventral Relating to the venter, the outer surface of the whorl of a cephalopod.

vertebrate A creature with a backbone.

whorl The coil of a shell, especially used of cephalopods.

zone A small unit of geological time. A number of zones make up a period. In some parts of the time scale zones are of one million years or less in length. Each zone is named after an index fossil. This fossil is chosen because it occurs only during the time represented by the rocks of that zone.

BIBLIOGRAPHY

This listing is intended to offer useful guidance for additional reading, rather than to provide an exhaustive survey of the literature on the subject. By consulting the bibliographies in the books listed below, you can extend your knowledge even further.

Barthel K.W., Swinburne N.H.M. and Conway Morris S. *Solnhofen, a study in Mesozoic Palaeontology*, Cambridge University Press, 1990.

Benton M.J., *Fossil Record*, Chapman and Hall, London, 1993.

Benton M.J., *Vertebrate Palaeontology*, Chapman and Hall, London, 1995.

Benton M.J. and Spencer P.S., *Fossil Reptiles in Great Britain*, Chapman and Hall, London, 1995.

British Museum (Natural History), *British Caenozoic Fossils*, London, 1982.

British Museum (Natural History), *British Mesozoic Fossils*, London 1982.

British Museum (Natural History), *British Palaeozoic Fossils*, London, 1982.

Bromley R., *Trace Fossils*, Chapman and Hall, London, 1995.

Clarkson E.K.M., *Invertebrate Palaeontology and Evolution*, Allen and Unwin, London, 1979.

Donovan S.K., *The Process of Fossilisation*, Belhaven Press, London, 1990.

Gould S.J., *Wonderful Life, The Burgess Shale and the Nature of History*, Norton, New York, 1989.

Halstead L.B., *Evolution of Mammals*, Lowe, London, 1978.

Halstead L.B., *Hunting the Past*, Hamish Hamilton, London, 1982.

Lapidus D.F., *Collins Dictionary of Geology*, Collins, London, 1990.

Levi-Setti R., *Trilobites*, University of Chicago Press, 1993.

Locksley M., *Tracking Dinosaurs*, Cambridge University Press, Cambridge, 1991.

Long J.A. and Young G.C., *Fossil Fishes*, Chapman and Hall, London, 1995.

McKerrow W.S., *The Ecology of Fossils*, Duckworth, London, 1978.

Miles, R.S., *Palaeozoic Fishes*, Chapman Hall, London, 1971.

Moore R.C., *Treatise on Invertebrate Palaeontology*, University of Kansas, 1953 onwards.

Morton J.E., *Molluscs*, Hutchinson, London, 1967.

Murray J.W., *Atlas of Invertebrate Macrofossils*, Longman, Harlow, Essex, 1985.

Norman D., *Illustrated Encyclopedia of Dinosaurs*, Salamander, London, 1985.

Pellant C., *Earthscope*, Salamander, London, 1985.

Pellant C. *Rocks, Minerals and Fossils of the World*, Pan, London 1990.

Pinna G., *The Dawn of Life*, World Publishing, New York, 1972.

Ransom J.E., *Fossils in America*, Harper and Row, New York, 1964.

Romer A.S., *Vertebrate Palaeontology*, University of Chicago Press, 1966.

Rudwick M.J.S., *Living and Fossil Brachiopods*, Hutchinson, London, 1970.

Tucker Abbott R., *Seashells of the Northern Hemisphere*, Dragon's World, London, 1990.

Whitten D.G.A. and Brooks J.R.V., *The Penguin Dictionary of Geology*, Penguin, London, 1990.

The various geological and palaeontological societies publish a number of journals. Membership of these societies is of value to amateurs as well as professional geologists. The body of palaeontological knowledge is frequently enriched by contributions from newcomers to the field. One journal that is particularly appropriate for the amateur as well as the professional is *Geology Today*, published by Blackwell Scientific Publications, Oxford, UK. This frequently covers topics of palaeontological interest.

Page numbers in *italic* type refer
to illustrations and photographs.

ACKNOWLEDGEMENTS

This book has involved the help and advice of many people, both professional geologists and amateurs. Members of the geology department at the University of Keele, Staffordshire UK, where I was an undergraduate many years ago, have helped greatly. Hugh Torrens allowed access to specimens from the Keele collection for reference and photography, and also let me borrow material from his own collection. He has always been forthcoming with advice on palaeontological and many other subjects. The depth and breadth of his knowledge never ceases to amaze me. Phil Lane allowed me access to trilobites at Keele and David Stevenson gave advice on echinoderms.

I have been allowed to photograph and study fossils from many other collections. The fine fossils in the Cleveland County collection have been provided by the curator, Ken Sedman, who has given helpful advice and details about his collection. He has also provided books, maps and periodicals for my use. At the National Museum of Wales, Bob Owens made trilobites from their magnificent collection available for photography and at the Royal Museum of Scotland, In Edinburgh, Ian Rolfe gave me access to the unrivalled collection of Devonian fish. At the Leeds City Museum, Jim Nunney provided excellent material for photography, as did Don Steward at the City Museum, Stoke-on-Trent, Staffordshire.

Many people have allowed me to study and photograph their private collections. I am particularly indebted to Jeff Mullroy of Great Ayton, Cleveland, whose great enthusiasm for palaeontology has produced a wonderful, expertly curated, ever expanding, collection. Sid Weatherill, of Whitby, John Fraser, of Leeds, Mike Marshall of Whitby, Becky Waters of Middlesbrough, and Lisa Crone of Thornaby have all helped with specimens and in other ways.

Without constant encouragement and unstinting help from my wife, Helen, the book would never have been completed and would probably be in a language which only vaguely resembles decent English. She has a meticulous eye for detail when proof-reading and her untiring help in cataloguing shots during photographic sessions not only saved countless hours of my time, but also ensured that we have a set of captions which could be read. My three children have helped in a variety of ways. Daniel is far more versed in the mysteries of my word processor than I, and has often sorted out problems, usually of my own making. Adam has provided musical background to writing with guitar riffs, and Emily has been known to change the colour of what little hair I still have, though whether this has helped work on the book is debatable!